How the Truth Could Hurt

"I've got years of love saved up for you, Madison," she said.

He grabbed at her hands and moved his lips to her ear, desperate to make her understand. "I want to wake up with you beside me in the morning, sweetheart. I want to come home to you. I want to build myself around you."

Her whole body went stiff with hurt as she froze in his arms. "You want?" she said icily. *"You want?* What about what I want?"

LINDA SHAW
is the mother of three children and enjoys her life in Keene, Texas, which she shares with her husband. When Linda isn't writing romantic novels, she's practicing or teaching the piano, violin, or viola.

Dear Reader,

Silhouette Special Editions are an exciting new line of contemporary romances from Silhouette Books. Special Editions are written specifically for our readers who want a story with heightened romantic tension.

Special Editions have all the elements you've enjoyed in Silhouette Romances and *more*. These stories concentrate on romance in a longer, more realistic and sophisticated way, and they feature greater sensual detail.

I hope you enjoy this book and all the wonderful romances from Silhouette. We welcome any suggestions or comments and invite you to write to us at the address below.

Karen Solem
Editor-in-Chief
Silhouette Books
P.O. Box 769
New York, N. Y. 10019

LINDA SHAW
After the Rain

Silhouette Special Edition

Published by Silhouette Books New York

America's Publisher of Contemporary Romance

Other Silhouette Books by Linda Shaw

December's Wine
All She Ever Wanted

SILHOUETTE BOOKS, a Simon & Schuster Division of
GULF & WESTERN CORPORATION
1230 Avenue of the Americas, New York, N.Y. 10020

ISBN: 0-671-53567-6

First Silhouette Books printing January, 1983

10 9 8 7 6 5 4 3 2 1

Map by Ray Lundgren

SILHOUETTE, SILHOUETTE SPECIAL EDITION
and colophon are trademarks of Simon & Schuster.

America's Publisher of Contemporary Romance

Printed in the U.S.A.

To Zina and Rob,
two of my dearest

After the Rain

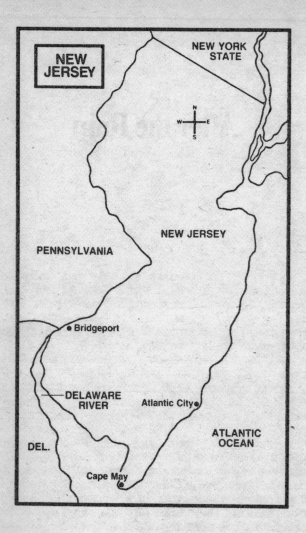

Chapter One

As Patrice Harrows coasted down a side road fifty miles north of Atlantic City, a layer of fine dust powdered over the Ferrari until it changed color. She had just washed the car, but that didn't matter. The Ferrari was a punishing, self-inflicted symbol of the worst mistake of her life. She despised it.

Swerving, she avoided a nasty hole in the road. Two pieces of unopened mail scuttled across the seat and slipped to the floor: the final papers of her divorce and her Master's diploma of law. *The end and the beginning,* she reflected with wry, twenty-five-year-old resignation.

What a colossal waste her marriage to Justin Harrows had been! She hadn't even married Justin for his inherited fortune, which was enormous. She had married The Name; Justin Cunningham Harrows III, son of a philanthropist, executor of his father's celebrated trust, owner of *The Atlantic City Telegram*. Three years ago she had married a man she didn't love because her parents had wanted it badly.

And the Ferrari? All sixty thousand dollars of it? The Ferrari was her parents' unwanted, four-wheeled penance for all the months of subtle pressuring. She drove it because it kept her humble. It mocked her. It reminded her that wealth and beauty were only superficial, that beneath them she was, after all, only too human.

Ah well, she thought, she would survive the divorce. Sometimes she felt she could survive anything. It was the ultimate order of life, wasn't it? Something ending, something beginning out of its ashes? Only the beginning would be different than she had expected.

"A normal pregnancy," her obstetrician had approved two months ago as he pleasantly smoothed his well-fed girth. "You'll have a blond, green-eyed angel, Patrice, just like yourself."

"She'll have a bit more backbone than her mother, I hope," Patrice added with a regretful knitting of her ash-colored brows.

"Really, Patrice, you must tell Justin you're pregnant," her mother had advised days later. "I don't care if you two are divorcing. The man has a right to know."

"Justin and I are finished, Mother," Patrice told her emphatically, though Betty Clayburne still chafed at being reminded. "We should never have begun."

Betty predictably defended Justin. "I'll admit he's made his mistakes, Patty, but he's such a young man. A baby could be the maturing of him. You can't keep something like this from a man."

Standing up to her mother had never come easily to Patrice. Not even in her most rebellious teenage years had she openly defied her. Now, after months of grueling self-discipline, she could smile. Unwaveringly polite, she said, "This is my baby, not Justin's, not anyone's. It cost me a lot to become single again, Mother. I intend to remain that way."

"You'll change your mind."

"If I do, it'll be my choice this time, not my family's."

Patrice's cherished self-assertion, restrained though it was, was not lost on Betty. She drew herself up, lovely and queenlike. "You've grown cold the past year, Patrice. Very . . . cold."

"I know." Patrice had countered her mother without a single heartbeat of hesitation. "Justin was an incredibly capable teacher."

Now the powerful Ferrari engine snarled as Patrice streaked down the road toward the outskirts of an insignificant little town. With slender fingers curled about the steering wheel, handling the big car with skill, Patrice considered her immediate task: her first case.

Until six weeks ago no one paid any attention to the town of Bridgeport, New Jersey. It was just there—a peaceful rural community, many of whose breadwinners commuted into Atlantic City to work during the day and to play at night. Bulldozers now leveled a vast ten-acre building site within the city limits. Steel girders outlined the skeleton of a gargantuan manufacturing complex, the reason why her own boss, attorney Adam Wentworth, had sent her out here today. Citizen protest in Bridgeport had exploded to a loud and public outcry. Remcon, Incorporated, was building at the back door of the town.

"They'll ruin our land and kill our children with their TCP!" men shouted to newspapers and anyone else who would listen.

"We'll have another Love Canal up here!" they had yelled into the telephone to the aging Adam Wentworth. "We need a lawyer. Send one. Quick!"

This incident was the first, full-fledged legal suit Patrice had handled on her own. The prospects of it excited her, challenged her until her scalp tingled with anticipation. She wanted to prove to herself that she truly could be independent of her family, especially from Justin and his degrading insinuations. She only wished she felt better today. All morning a troublesome ache had plagued the small of her back.

Wriggling uncomfortably in the seat, she slowed the car and steered toward a parked van with KZAT-TV plastered across its side. Its doors gaped open, and it was flanked by a semicircle of men and women trudging along the fringes of the site. WE DON'T WANT YOU! read several handpainted posters slung across their shoulders. REMCON, TAKE YOUR POLLUTION SOMEWHERE ELSE! demanded others.

From her car Patrice could see the woman reporter talking into her microphone. Beside her hovered a young man, a minicam sprouting out of his shoulder. *This is really the acid test,* she told herself apprehensively. She wondered, now that she was about to walk into it, if her first case would involve a full-blown riot.

Flicking off the ignition, she stepped resolutely onto the grassless crust of sunbaked land. She removed her tortoiseshell glasses and replaced them with a huge pair of Foster Grants. The August sun beat relentlessly upon her head.

At the growl of a motorcycle sputtering up behind the Ferrari, Patrice twisted to watch a tall, bearded man swing off the machine. He kicked out its stand and, without glancing at her, strode rapidly toward the construction site several hundred yards away. He lifted off his helmet as he walked and threaded his fingers through a mane of thick black hair.

Dismissing him, Patrice took a final courageous breath. She approached the gathered protesters. The man holding the minicam advanced several steps toward her, his camera aimed directly at her, then retreated as she walked toward him.

Through the lens the cameraman focused upon an extraordinarily pretty woman, conservatively dressed though lusciously tall and slender. She was the photogenic type of woman who made any cameraman look like a genius. He captured the fluid grace of her two-piece beige suit as she moved. Then he zoomed in upon her face. Thick blond hair knotted severely at the back of her head in a classical fashion not every woman could wear. Though he couldn't see her eyes behind the dark glasses, he guessed they, too, were beautiful. Her one marring feature was her coloring; she was dreadfully pale, despite the lip gloss and peach-tinted blusher she wore.

With a practiced glance Patrice sized up the volatile potential of the situation she found herself in. She flexed her throbbing back and steeled herself as a microphone was thrust rudely in her face. The reporter immediately asked who she was.

"Patrice Harrows. I'm the attorney on this case."

"Would you care to make a comment, Miss Harrows?"

"Mrs. Harrows, and no, I would not. I just got here. Would you mind turning off that camera, please?" She gestured to the wary cameraman. "I need a few minutes to talk to these people. After that, if a statement's necessary, I'll make one."

Once the townspeople realized their attorney had arrived, most of them lowered their posters and ambled toward her. They gathered in a dusty, disorganized circle, their faces pinched, though hopeful, and their clothes wilted from the heat of the sun.

"The next thing you know"—a housewife in blue jeans offered her unsolicited opinion—"we'll be having to move away from our homes, just like they did in New York."

A local grocer braced knobby fists on his hips. "I've checked into this company. Remcon's got one lawsuit pending right now, for dumping waste into the Mississippi River."

"Look, Tom. Two of their big shots're coming."

A woman pointed as two dark-suited men stepped from an officious-looking black car that had nosed in beside the Ferrari. Talking between themselves, heads bent, occasionally glancing up at the gathered protesters, the pair advanced toward the gathered crowd.

"Get out!" screamed the distraught woman, waving her arms. "Take your kidney complaints and your deformed babies and get out!"

Grabbing one of the woman's arms, Patrice shook her head. "That won't help," she cautioned.

The woman grudgingly moved to stand beside a short, stocky man who placed his arm about her shoulders. Patrice wondered if the woman was pregnant, too. Would she be standing out here herself if she lived in Bridgeport, New Jersey?

One of the Remcon men, his face as youthfully smooth as a boy's, extended his hand. Assessing him, Patrice politely shook it.

"My name is Phil Anthony," he explained. "I'm the attorney for Remcon, and this is Robert Sterling, the vice-president in charge of field affairs. You represent Wentworth? We heard"—he threw out a disdainful hand—"that they called in some counsel."

Patrice nodded. Bracing her case upon her hip as a writing surface, she scribbled the men's names in a small notebook.

The hush that descended as she wrote was unanticipated, startling everyone. Her pen stopped moving, and as her head snapped up in those first seconds of quiet, she realized that no one was shouting anymore. The protesters muffled their complaints, and everyone peered out at the construction site.

Work was grinding to a crucial halt. The great crane, hoisting a steel beam as if it were a twig, settled it slowly into place. The bulldozer operators climbed down from the heavy equipment. Men began streaming off the gaunt framework of the construction. Except for the occasional slam of a pickup door, silence hung curiously heavy.

"We're halting construction temporarily," Robert Sterling noted with a falsely benevolent smile. "Remcon doesn't want adverse publicity. We'll do everything within our power to work with the people of Bridgeport."

Not believing a word he said, Patrice smiled, too. "That's good thinking."

The smile faded as the vice-president unbuttoned his suit coat and dragged a finger beneath the pinch of his collar. He disliked the woman attorney on principle. "But the people need to understand what Remcon can do for the town."

"I'm sure they do understand," Patrice interjected.

Sterling's annoyance reddened his neck. Perspiration glinted on the ridge of his cheekbones. "The facility will bring growth to the town. It will create new jobs and bring in other industry."

"What good will that do if we have to spend millions cleaning up your chemical waste?" a thin man with massive, heavily veined hands complained. "I want growth as much as the next person, but not at this cost."

"Yeah, Mr. Sterling. What's a job worth if you're dying of leukemia?"

Patrice turned toward the people, irritably aware that the camera was rolling again. "I will see a committee of six in my office tomorrow morning. We'll draw up a formal complaint at that time. Your voices must be channeled through the government and the EPA to be effective. And you, Mr. Sterling, would be well advised to keep your construction ceased until we can get some kind of ruling from the courts."

Robert Sterling shifted his weight, anxious to leave the dust of the place. "What we do, we do voluntarily. There is no injunction against us, you realize."

"Of course."

After several minutes the crowd agreed to present themselves as a committee at the firm of Adam Wentworth.

Nodding, feeling feverish and wishing desperately to sit down, Patrice passed out several business cards and began walking back to the Ferrari. At least Remcon was leaving, too, she consoled herself. This situation wouldn't detonate today.

She glanced up as the reporter fell into step beside her.

"What will the city of Bridgeport do, Mrs. Harrows, if the Remcon officials refuse to stop construction?" the woman asked.

"The people of this town have the right to be heard. If the city council isn't sensitive to their complaints, they may find themselves under attack, as well as Remcon."

"Aren't you the daughter of Simon Clayburne, the gambling magnate who's opening the Atlantis II downtown?"

Patrice frowned at the question. Simon Clayburne hated being referred to as a "gambling man," though, in fact, he was one. He was opening a plush new casino and stringently regulated hotel in the resort area of Atlantic City. Simon's wealth was probably greater than even he knew. He had played his part in urging the marriage of the older Clayburne daughter to the vastly respectable Harrows heir because money couldn't buy the things he wanted: social acceptance and approval.

Patrice answered grudgingly. "Yes."

"And isn't your husband *the* Justin Harrows who owns *The Atlantic City Telegram?*"

The look Patrice shot the reporter warned her that she had no intentions of commenting upon her personal life. As she left she heard the reporter refreshing the memory of her viewers of the "three-year-old marriage of the Clayburne millions to the enormous Harrows trust."

The Harrows Foundation was always news. The Garland Harrows' money was responsible for a number of the cultural restorations in the city and several medical and social facilities as well. Because of the foundation's work, her marriage to Justin had attracted the media too many times before. She wearied of being under the microscope of the press.

The Ferrari, Patrice thought as she neared it, was farther away than she remembered. Her legs hurt with every step. When she finally slid onto the seat, her hands shook so badly she couldn't fit the key into the slot of the ignition. Dear God! She dropped her forehead onto the leather-covered steering wheel and wished she were home.

However, she swallowed down the nausea swimming up into her throat. She inserted the key, successfully this time. Glancing briefly into the rearview mirror, she veered the wheel and backed the car around.

The sound of metal crunching unexpectedly with metal sent her foot slamming to the brake. Horrified, she jerked forward. Again, there was a hideous metallic shredding as the car lurched to a humiliating stop.

Battling an odd hysteria, for Patrice's one pride was her incontestable composure, she stepped swiftly from the car. Her lips parted and her jaw dropped loosely. Five feet from her rear bumper lay a crumpled heap of twisted machinery—what had once been a smartly rigged Kawasaki KZ750.

"Oh, Lord," she whimpered, wide eyed.

The noise of impact lasted only a few seconds, but it attracted the people gathered about the television van. With the camera running, they slithered toward her like curious shavings to a magnet. Amid their gesturing and garbled questions, Patrice shoved the Foster Grants back on her nose to hide the desperation welling in her eyes. At the sight of the tall, bearded figure striding irately from the construction site, she slumped in defeat.

The man was in a furious temper. His frayed jeans flapped threateningly about long legs, and a scarred motorcycle helmet dangled by its strap from one hand. The other hand, balled into a tight fist, swung beside him. The groove that creased his forehead promised the unmitigated worst!

Though Patrice could see little of the man behind the beard, she knew his teeth were grinding. What could she say? The whole thing was plainly her fault. How could she have been so untypically careless?

"Lady!" He yelled the word like an obscene epithet. His fist, as he walked, transformed itself into an accusing finger. He towered over the hopeless shambles, his nostrils thinned in outrage.

Facing her, he said, "You missed the crash bars, dear. Don't you want to pull up and have one more try at it?"

He acted as if she had purposely done it, and with more an act of instinct than reason, Patrice drew herself regally upward. Her stance was unknowingly haughty, fiery with resilience. The man's eyes, starkly blue in contrast to his black hair and beard, raked over her posture with affront.

He was too slender, Patrice thought, and a good half head taller than she, which was different since not all men were. There was nothing particularly outstanding about his looks that she could see in her distraught state. Yet a definite power was in his bearing. She gave little credence to physical beauty—Justin was beautiful —but she prudently respected power. So, riveting her eyes on his sneakers, which had seen better days, she spoke with a valiant effort at courtesy.

"I take full responsibility, sir," she began and turned from him, meaning to reach into her car for her handbag.

His deep voice rumbled indignantly in his chest. "You'll what?"

"I'll pay whatever you say!" she yelled back, exasperated, visibly struggling to control herself. Her spread hands were thrust outward. "I'm sorry! You didn't have to park the thing on my rear bumper!"

"It was parked where it belonged. What d'you think your damned mirror's for?"

"I looked. And that machine was . . . was—"

He might have said something else; Patrice didn't know. The August sun persistently probed into her scalp, and her toes prickled with electrical warnings. Up through the large bones of her legs a new and different pain splintered and centered itself deep in the recesses of her belly. Blurring about her feet, as villainously black as the angry man's beard, a darkness smeared into his sneakers then melted into his pants. Everything dimmed, even the clarity of the daylight. Her hands clawed futilely at the agony ripping through her body.

The last thing Patrice realized, besides the liquid buckling of her knees, was the slide of her sunglasses down the bridge of her nose.

Madison Brannen, when he lunged forward to catch the woman before she could actually hit the ground, suffered a mixture of masculine embarrassment and surprise. Hotheadedness was something he intensely disliked in other people, but his own worst failing was saying too much, too fast. Still, he found it difficult to believe he had frightened her that much!

He staggered beneath her weight.

Though she was slender, she was not small. Picking her up as he was forced to do, taking the full brunt of her weight upon his legs, hurt him. The steel pins running through both his knees—bitter trophies from a mine field in Vietnam—flared with a fiery pain at the demands suddenly forced upon them.

Patrice's head draped back over Madison's arm. Her hair, loosening itself, flowed over his shoulder to shimmer in a golden froth. Her well-curved lips were parted. Pale cheeks stretched over high, aristocratic bones. Starkly white, she looked like death.

The television camera zoomed in upon them.

"Ladies and gentlemen," droned the reporter, "a startling . . ."

"Will you get rid of that damned thing?" Madison barked. He glanced urgently about himself. The nearest car was the Remcon staff car. Stepping toward it, he choked down a harsh breath.

"What happened?"

Phil Anthony rushed up behind Madison. He took one look at the corded muscles straining down the sides of Madison's neck and whipped open the backseat of the car. "Stand back, please," he ordered the onlookers. Then more tersely, "Please, give us room!"

Ignoring the press of the curious observers, Madison maneuvered himself into the backseat of Robert Sterling's Lincoln Continental. Still holding Patrice cradled against his chest, he slumped back against the seat. The Remcon attorney, without asking questions, got the operator on the car telephone and ordered an ambulance.

Robert Sterling leaned an immaculately combed head through the open door and peered over the seat at Patrice. "What do you suppose is wrong with her?" he asked and unconsciously adjusted his tie. "Diabetic, maybe?"

Shaking his head at Sterling's question, Madison moistened his lips. "Don't know," he said. "I just hope that ambulance doesn't take all day."

"It's on the way." Phil Anthony slumped back against the seat to catch his breath. "You look terrible, Brannen. What'd you do, come straight from the campsite?"

Madison's lips curled into a crooked grimace at the mention of his unkempt appearance. "The first vacation I've had in five years," he remarked dryly, "and I can't even get in the front door to change my clothes.

20

What are you guys trying to do up here, start a war? Who is this woman?"

"The opposition, my man." Phil chuckled. Then he sobered. "The opposition."

The youthful counselor eagerly spouted the same newsworthy gossip as the television reporter had told her video audience. Madison, grasping little more than Patrice's name and the publicized status of Justin Harrows, shifted his body. He attempted to arrange his limp female burden more comfortably on the empty side of the seat.

"She needs a blanket—" he started to say before his eyes flared with alarm.

Patrice's blood seeped into the folds of her beige skirt and spread over her legs, free-flowing and fresh. Madison automatically looked at his shirt. Streaks of bright red soaked its front and stained one sleeve.

A horrible sensation of déjà vu washed over Madison. For grisly seconds he was caught back in the time lock of Southeast Asia, carrying a dying buddy through the sweating jungle. The flashback had tormented him many times before. The reality was as amazingly vivid now as it had been years ago. *This isn't Nam!* he reminded himself harshly and forced himself into the present. There was no artillery, no hills, no heat. There was only home. Today.

"My, God!" he breathed and caught the eye of the talkative Remcon attorney. Frightfully aware of his male ineptness in this situation, he said, "Get the ambulance on the horn, Anthony. Tell them we'll meet 'em halfway."

He was thirty-five years old, Madison reflected when he braced the heels of his feet against the sway of the ambulance. He had lived through a war. He had lain awake to the thunder of heavy artillery. He had shivered at the whine of a sniper's gun. Yet he hated the wail of a siren more than anything he knew.

Arranging his cramped legs nearer the oxygen tanks, he watched the ambulance attendant monitor Patrice's pulse. After a moment the gaunt-faced man removed the stethoscope from his ears and let it slip free about his neck.

"Your wife?" he asked Madison as he forced open Patrice's unseeing eyes, one at a time.

Madison thought the medic vaguely resembled a mountain goat, yet the voice behind the face was kind, competent. He shook his head. "Never saw her before today," he replied. "She fainted right at my feet."

"Oh. Sorry. When you said you thought she might be pregnant, I just assumed . . . Well, that's pretty involved anyway. Most people don't like to get involved."

Smiling, Madison ruefully recalled his ruined Kawasaki. "We're involved. Sort of."

"Good-looking lady."

With an unthinking gesture Madison tugged at the scruff of his beard. Being aware of a woman's physical attributes when she lay unconscious seemed nothing short of obscene. But it would have taken a superman to ignore the mature curves of her breasts as they steadily rose and fell beneath the sheet. Or the willowy outline of her legs, the delicate curl of her fingers, her smell. Especially her smell; he could drown in it. He supposed he really was involved with Mrs. Patrice Harrows in a way. And he'd noticed how pretty she was, married or not.

"Yeah," he agreed wryly as he watched for Patrice to make any indication of returning to consciousness. "I feel like a heel noticing."

From the front of the ambulance the driver radioed in their location, and the radio spit static back at him. Madison leaned into the shrieking curve as the vehicle careened through downtown Atlantic City.

If Patrice Harrows represented the hue and cry of

Bridgeport, that made them natural enemies, he figured. His own engineering firm had just contracted to construct some of the interior of Remcon's proposed plant. Part of his responsibility as owner of the firm was to work closely with the Remcon executives, to make certain that the company satisfied the requirements of the Environmental Protection Agency.

And this woman whose blood was drying on his own shirt? She was little Snow White fighting a losing battle against giants. The battle between industry and the environment had been fought many times: the Goliath Corporation versus the Lady Lawyer. He guessed she didn't have a chance. The absolute last thing in the world he should be doing was sitting beside her, caring what happened to her.

Patrice's return to consciousness was gradual. When she blinked her eyes, immediately aware of the tormented wail of the siren, she didn't need anyone to explain what had happened. The growing sensibility of her pain told her that. Focusing on the bearded man beside her, she moaned into the oxygen mask that covered her nose.

He leaned forward. He spoke with a cautious precision. "Mrs. Harrows, do you remember me?"

She struck at the plastic device on her face and dislodged it, nodding at him. His steely fingers closed about her wrist as he shook his head and readjusted the mask.

"My name is Madison Brannen," he said. "I found your mother's name with your ID. Someone called her, I think. She should be at the hospital by the time we get there."

When Patrice opened her eyes again, as the paramedic was checking her blood pressure, Madison Brannen had moved farther away. He seemed troubled by his untidy appearance. He was straightening his shirt, which had fallen open halfway to his waist. He buttoned it until only fine wisps of dark hair furled above its neck, then tucked it beneath his belt. As he combed his fingers through the tousled locks of hair he realized she was looking at him.

He paused. "You're going to be fine," he said awkwardly and dropped his hands to his knees.

She hardly had time to think about his hair, which grew rebelliously long, or the neat symmetry of his hands. A new pain knifed through her. As she clawed into the sides of the stretcher her knuckles whitened.

"I'm going to lose this baby," she groaned into the mask.

Shaking his craggy head at her, the attendant released the band from about her arm. "Step on it, Mac," he called to the driver.

With a mute, helpless regard, Patrice watched the paramedic. Then she stared at the drawn, unyielding profile of the bearded cyclist. Even in her distress she recognized his deliberate, frowning detachment. They were total strangers, yet she would have welcomed the comfort of his words, no matter what they were. But he offered nothing. He sat hunched beside the oxygen tanks, withdrawn into himself.

Madison wasn't oblivious to Patrice's need for his comfort. It beckoned to him, like the scent of her perfume. But several things had to be considered, he figured, not only for himself but for her. In time she would learn who he was, that he was on the "other side."

Too, she was married. That fact shouldn't mean anything, but it did. He had carried her in his arms, and for brief moments her blood had joined them together. Perhaps that was an outdated loyalty stemming from the war when they had all carried each other and had shared blood and the murky fear of dying. Still, Patrice Harrows wasn't just any woman now.

The best way to handle this situation, he decided,

was to remain an impersonal observer. He would do what he could to help, but he would keep his sympathies on a purely objective plane. If he were smart, he would smile; he would reassure her that everything would be all right and refuse to look at her pale, haunting face again.

The ambulance lurched. In her haze of suffering, Patrice whimpered.

Madison's hand instinctively reached out, then swiftly drew back. He flicked his tongue across the tension of his mouth. His hand scoured across his face as her fingers opened and shut with desperation.

Patrice's blind groping unraveled all of Madison's reasoning with the capriciousness of a kitten slapping a ball of yarn. Despite all his private attempts to be logical, his hard tanned fingers laced through her trembling, searching ones. When she felt the underlying strength of his grip, her eyes gradually opened as if he had spoken aloud to her.

Help me, her blurring tears begged him as his beard filled her vision.

His cheek lowered to press gently against hers, and she relaxed, giving herself up to his solace. He was a stranger helping another stranger, she thought, one person caring about another. She sought his strength like a drowning person grappling for the promise of a lifeline and crushed his hands with a frenzied power she didn't ordinarily possess.

Amazed, Madison winced.

"Just a few more minutes, dear." His calm, old-fashioned words fell against her ear. "You can make it. I'll stay with you." His breath was warm and mellow on her jaw, fortifying her by its very presence.

Her moan came involuntarily.

"You're doing great," he said. Now he was hurting for her, and with her. "Really great."

"The pain . . ." she gasped.

25

"I know what pain is. It makes the minutes much longer than they are. But the doctors'll give you something soon, and it won't hurt anymore."

"Thank you," she whispered with the honesty of the helpless.

The tension in his face relented somewhat, but Patrice didn't see it. "I live dangerously," he said bleakly.

Though she didn't understand exactly what he meant, certainly not that Madison Brannen was suffering a swift, instinctual dislike for her husband who should be in his place, helping her, she attempted to smile.

"I didn't mean to wreck your Kawasaki," she choked.

Smiling lopsidedly, he dismissed the motorcycle. He was finding himself unable to pretend that he wasn't already getting himself in too deeply with her. If in the weeks ahead he and this woman battled each other—legally, publicly—he would deal with it then. Now he just didn't want her to die. And, for some horrible, nightmarish moment, he was afraid she might. He murmured every word of encouragement he knew, anything he could think of to lengthen her endurance. Whether or not it helped, he had no idea. But he didn't move from beside her until the ambulance screamed its final warning, braked and began backing its cumbersome shape beneath the canopy of the emergency room of the hospital.

Chapter Two

The bell of a doctor's page chimed twice.

Betty Clayburne, seized by the bittersweet memories one recalls in a time of crisis, shivered. She wondered, as her eyes adhered to the door of the recovery room, how many people had passed through the doors of the hospital since its founding. Both her daughters had been born in this hospital; now one could die here.

When a doctor dressed in crumpled surgery greens strode down the hall, Betty felt for the arm of Patrice's sister. Cathy stirred wearily. The two women had been waiting nearly three hours for word of Patrice's condition.

Sympathetically Cathy drew her mother to her feet. "Let's get a drink of water," she said and gestured toward a fountain down the hall.

Cathy Webster wore her affluence as naturally as her mother did, a habit of a lifetime. But hospitals had a way of stripping away such things as physical beauty. Cartier jewelry and designer dresses didn't separate them now from other anxious families who waited for a prognosis too long in coming.

Betty, stiffened from long hours of sitting, stretched herself tiredly. "Why is *that man* still here?"

Following Betty's stare down the tiled corridor near the fountain, Cathy observed Madison Brannen slouched low on his spine on a straight-backed chair. The clean patrician features of the man's nose, the broad intelligent forehead and brows, clashed noticeably with the disorder of his clothes. The manner in which he carried himself projected a definite authority —something a man either had or didn't have. Even the scuffed sneakers jutting out in front of him didn't detract from his air of confidence. Though they had spoken only briefly outside the emergency entrance, Cathy suspected Mr. Brannen was anything except what he seemed.

"He's not hurting anything," she defended him in an indulgent, scolding tone. She matched her steps to her mother's prim ones. "Are you hungry? Want a sandwich?"

Shaking her head, Betty fished in her bag for a compact. After giving her mirror a dissatisfied pout, she snapped it closed.

"Thank you no, darling. But you're considerate to ask. Tell me, Cathy, how does Patrice manage to pick up strays like that? You never did. I've never understood how two girls could be so completely different."

"Why? Because I'm predictable? Because I have a husband who works for a state senator? Two daughters? A house? Two cars? Oh, Mother, come on."

Betty cast her a reproving glance. "Don't knock predictability. I need one daughter I can count on."

Interrupting them, two orderlies hurriedly wheeled a stretcher down the hall between them. Cathy spoke over it. "You could count on Patrice, Mother, if you'd give her half a chance."

The casual flick of a ringed hand was characteristic of Betty. "*He* is one reason. Why does she associate with such people? The man is probably a vagrant. Look at those clothes, that *hair!* One thing you'll have to admit, Cathy, Justin is first class. Always."

Cathy agreed with an ironic, distant stare. "Yes, you're right. Every time Justin hurts Patrice, he does it with finesse."

Madison lifted his chin from its resting place upon the broad expanse of his chest and smothered a yawn. He glanced obliquely at the two women coming directly toward him. Though not introduced, he knew exactly who they were.

Patrice Harrows' mother didn't like him, he knew. From the moment he had crawled out of the ambulance none of Betty Clayburne's frowning disapproval had been lost on him. He had followed the stretcher to the swinging doors of the emergency room where he was brusquely informed he could go no further. There, as he stood helplessly in the hallway, Betty had let him know with the angle of her chin that he was no longer needed or wanted. He wouldn't have been surprised if she had offered to pay him like a taxi driver and had told him to keep the change.

"Pardon me," Cathy Webster said, smiling as she stepped around his feet.

Returning the pleasant smile, Madison pulled his body upright. He tucked his stained denim shirt into the waist of his jeans and moved his feet from their path. He was about to speak when both women stopped walking. Instinctively he followed the direction of their gaze.

Striding rapidly down the hallway, a sport jacket slung over one shoulder, curly brown hair framing a sublimely angelic face, was one of the best-looking men Madison had ever seen. He watched the man's mouth curve into an arresting, diplomatic smile. He knew, as certainly as one knows when a storm is electrifying the atmosphere, that he was Patrice Harrows' husband.

Why weren't you here when she needed you? he demanded silently, irrationally prejudiced. Then he felt foolish, thinking that the man must have come the moment he learned his wife was ill.

Rubbing his palms against the unfamiliar beard he wore, Madison avoided the scene of hugging and entwined arms, of whispered information and looks of entreaty. Even if it were illogical, he thought, he was sure he would never, under any circumstances, like this man.

In the recovery room at the opposite end of the hall from where Madison sat nursing his resentment of Justin Harrows, Dr. Paul Nelson withdrew a chart from the foot of Patrice's bed. He studied his patient with something near respect on his face.

Bravery from a woman like her surprised him. Her pain, before the Pentothal had found her vein, had been more than most would tolerate before screaming for the needle. Her only outward sign of suffering had been a dark, folding-in upon herself.

"Bigot," he silently corrected himself. Rich and spoiled weren't always synonymous.

The data in his hand indicated the loss of a three-month fetus. General health—good. First pregnancy. Under normal circumstances Patrice had one of those peaches-and-cream complexions like the models in the fashion magazines. Now she was gray; her lips were parched and lax, revealing fascinating, slightly uneven teeth.

He took her pulse, then her blood pressure. "Has she tried to wake up?"

"Once," the nurse replied, watching closely as the doctor grasped the patient's chin firmly in his hand.

"Patrice!" he called sharply. He shook her head.

"Wake up, Patrice. Come on, babe. You're going to be all right. Wake up."

Rather ungently, he slapped her jaw. Patrice made an incoherent sound and wrenched her face away as her brain wandered up from the murky pits of artificial sleep.

"That's a good girl. Come on."

She moistened her lips. "Justin?" she called from her haze.

"This is Paul Nelson, Patrice. Do you know where you are?"

Her long lashes fluttered, then her eyes opened briefly to show him pupils so deeply green they looked mossy, liquid.

"What's your father's full name, Patrice?"

Her drugged reply sounded as if she dragged an enormous weight. "Simon Patrick Clayburne."

"What month is this?"

"Ahhh." She moistened her lips again, forming her answer with effort. "August." Limply her hand lifted, then dropped back to the sheet.

"Very good. You rest." Dr. Nelson gave her hand a bedside-mannerish pat, pleased with himself. "I'll be back in a few minutes."

"Wait," Patrice choked. Her mouth felt full of cotton, but dozens of questions thrashed in her mind. Her hands automatically moved to her abdomen. "I lost it, didn't I?"

Her eyes seemed to monopolize the whole of her pale, wondering face. Paul Nelson didn't hesitate to answer. Stepping to her bedside once again, fitting her chart beneath his arm, he gazed down at her with professional compassion.

"Yes, Patrice, you did. It was one of those freaky things that no one can explain. But there weren't any complications. Nothing is wrong inside you. There'll be other children."

31

For a moment her eyes filled, but she closed them so the tears did not spill. The doctor didn't attempt to soothe her but flicked a tissue from the box.

Patrice, blinking, waved the tissue away. "No, Paul. No more babies. I don't ever want to go through that again," she said.

"That feeling will go away in time."

Patrice had no energy to protest; the matter was none of his concern, anyway. As a way of changing the subject, she attempted to drag herself up onto her elbows. "I've got to get out of here," she fumed weakly. "I don't have time to be sick."

Paul looked like the king of Siam with his arms folded across his chest, her chart hugged between them. He lifted amused brows. "You really think you're up to that?"

"What did you give me? I'm as weak as a kitten." She glared at his advantage of being able to stand upright. "I really have to get out of here."

Replacing his bedside manner with an inflexible austerity he reserved for his most stubborn patients, the doctor unclipped his pen from a pocket already filled with pens. He scribbled something on her chart and replaced it.

"I'll have to see to your best interests myself, since you won't," he said evenly. "And if you don't use good sense, Mrs. Harrows, I'm going to instruct the nurse to give you a *real* shot."

"No shots!" she yelped, angry now. But she added more prudently, "Many people depend on me."

The doctor grinned. "Your clients will survive until you get on your feet. Adam Wentworth managed to carry on a law practice before he hired you. I suspect he'll make do."

"Don't give me bedside hype," she snapped and accused him with aggressive, piercing eyes.

"My, my," he teased. "I'm glad we aren't in court."

"When do I get out, doctor? Two days?"

"Three."

"I'm checking out of this hospital tomorrow."

Paul Nelson found Patrice stimulating, even sensual, in her protests. His finger touched the tip of a straight petulant nose, and Patrice moved her head, dodging further friendliness.

"I know you legal people," he intoned. "You think you know everything. If you get a secondary infection, you'll come crawling back on your hands and knees. Now, be a good girl and I'll dismiss you day after tomorrow."

Frowning, she retorted, "I'll have work sent in."

"Suit yourself," he said. "Just don't tie up the switchboard. And now"—he clicked his heels with military facetiousness—"I believe your mother is waiting to see you."

After Patrice's eyes followed the doctor's easy gait out into the hall, she didn't look at her nurse; she didn't want her spritely, overcheerful sympathy. Then, as if some invisible eraser passed across the fragile features, her face changed. Her green eyes dimmed, blurring in the oppressive depths of tears. Though she clenched her jaw in a supreme effort to control herself, she began trembling. She had wanted this baby more than she had ever wanted anything in her life.

She clamped her hands over her mouth, pressing hard. "Oh, God," she cried out deep inside her soul. "Oh, God, help me. I wish I had been the one to die. What am I going to do?"

Madison found the escape from the hospital floor an easy matter. But leaving the premises without knowing if Patrice was all right was another thing entirely. In fact, it was impossible.

Several times he had started to call himself a cab. Once he even dialed the telephone, but he couldn't bring himself to leave Patrice in that room. By the time visiting hours were ending he had explored all the grounds, roamed in and out of the snack bar a half-dozen times, drunk several cups of coffee that he didn't want, and finally leaned against one of the pillars outside and watched the sun go down.

At half-past nine o'clock he glumly decided to settle the debate with himself once and for all. If he were smart, he would walk out now and pretend this day had never happened. If he were a masochist—he could already hear the nagging advice of the Remcon executives—he would take the risk of embedding himself in Patrice Harrows' life a little more.

Madison paused before Patrice's door as if he half-way expected someone to come up behind him and caustically demand that he leave. He poked his bearded head inside the private room door. The head of the bed was elevated slightly. Patrice lay quite still, sleeping, her skin colorless. Her face, relaxed in slumber, was serenely framed by the mane of burnished gold hair.

He smiled at the nurse as she lifted her tired, care-lined face. "Visiting hours are over," she informed him quietly.

He presented the rest of his body and closed the door behind him. "Uh, yes, I was told that. But I . . ."

The nurse, laying aside her paperback novel, assumed her most forbidding scowl. "Are you a member of the family?"

"Yes," he lied with a perfectly guileless smile. "I'm her brother. I just got here from upstate. You don't mind if I come in for just a moment, do you? She'll be hurt if she learns I didn't come."

"I didn't know she had a brother."

The stern inspection she gave him, noting the blood-stained shirt, the rumpled clothes, the hair, was thoroughly skeptical. Madison was positive she believed he was the father of Patrice's baby. However, after she had considered it a moment, such a predicament apparently appealed to her sense of high adventure.

She retrieved her novel. "Just make it quick. I don't want the head nurse coming down on my head."

He flashed her a grateful smile. "You're really laid back, ma'am. You have my undying gratitude." When she crossed her legs and vainly smoothed her skirt, he smothered a smile and stepped beside the bed.

The presence of the nurse inhibited Madison, though. He would like to have touched Patrice's hand and told her he was sorry that she had lost her baby. He couldn't remember a time in his adult life when he hadn't wanted children. The nearest he had ever come was Miles, the small son of his sister. And to know a woman who had come so close, only to lose it, saddened him immeasurably.

Standing in relief against the starkness of the room—a rugged masculine oddity in all that sterile hospital order—he reached out a tenuous finger. When he touched a swirl of Patrice's hair, he stilled, as if he expected the nurse to say something. Very slowly he let out his breath.

He had no idea what he was doing here, nor where to go. He only knew that for some very unwelcome, unnecessary, and unnerving reason, he didn't want to leave. He felt grievously lonely.

Patrice stirred in her sleep. Unknowingly she kicked his thigh. Madison somberly pondered the toes that peeped from beneath the sheet to nestle against his leg. The sensation that shot through his body was one he hadn't experienced in years—not merely a sexual awareness but a strange, electrifying hunger for life. He thought that all those feelings had been killed in Vietnam.

He should go, he told himself. Behind him the nurse's cough was tactful but firm, urging him to leave. A little confused, much more drained than he thought, Madison replaced Patrice's foot beneath the sheet. It was his apology for turning away from her in the ambulance. Whatever happened between them in the coming weeks could easily be unpleasant. He honestly regretted that.

Letting his shoulders drop loosely, a stance that made his tall frame appear excessively weary, he lowered his head. Without a backward glance he let the door swoop shut behind him. Justin Harrows, he thought with remarkable prejudice, did not deserve to have this woman for his wife.

Chapter Three

$\mathscr{P}$atrice swung open the door of her refrigerator, caught it with a limber foot, and removed two eggs, a butter dish and a carton of sweet milk. Bumping it shut with a swivel of her hip, she moved toward the hardwood island in the center of the kitchen.

Above her, blissfully flaunting their copper bottoms, swung four long-handled pans. The circular table, which was actually a salvaged ice-cream-parlor castaway centered beneath an antique Tiffany lamp, was covered with a cheerful green cloth that swept the floor. It held one place mat and a paperback mystery. A flourishing philodendron rambled over the table, up the wall, and onto the dishwasher. Patrice loved this plant; she talked to it every day.

"Hello, Myrtle," she murmured now and bent fondly over its leaves. "Did you miss me while I was gone?"

Her words reminded her of her stay in the hospital. Still holding the eggs and milk, she straightened. She could have been entranced by some invisible Svengali as she stood perfectly immobile, staring at nothing, hardly breathing. She had only begun recalling the pain, the anesthesia, when the telephone rang.

She snapped instantly from the trance, set down the milk, and pinched the receiver between her shoulder and chin.

"Cathy!" She lifted down a pan. From habit she placed the eggs in it and stepped to the sink to fill it with water as she talked. "What's up?"

"You're okay." Her younger sister's voice sounded surprised.

"Did you expect me to be gasping for breath?"

Cathy giggled from the other end of the line. "I thought you might take advantage of the sympathy you've been getting and stay home a few more days. Did you go back to work today?"

Placing the pan of water on the stove, Patrice gave the teakettle a shake before turning on the burner. Her lips curved with self-mockery. "Everyone said 'Oh, you look so good, Patrice.' Which was only the polite way of saying they expected me to look horrible, of course. How're the girls?"

"Driving me crazy. Harold is never here when I need him."

What would her sister do if their circumstances were reversed? Patrice wondered. Perhaps then, Cathy might appreciate her good fortune in having borne two healthy daughters.

Eager to change the subject, Patrice reached behind herself for a stool and wearily climbed onto it. "I tried to track down that Mr. Brannen today," she said. "You remember him, from the hospital. Do you realize I demolished that poor man's bike? That'll cost me a pretty penny, I suppose. I have no idea what a new Kawasaki costs."

"I guess you know you're famous now."

"Oh?"

"You were on television with your Mr. Brannen. He

was carrying you to a car. Honestly, Patty, I thought Mother would freak out. Of course, I met the man and liked him, but I don't think Justin did. He took one look at him and swore several of those words only he knows."

Patrice sniffed at her opinions of Justin. "Justin thinks anyone who works for a living is beneath him. And the man is not *my* Mr. Brannen, Cath. I don't even know who he is. I thought he was a day laborer working at the construction site, but I called the crew foreman, and he said the man had never been on any of his payrolls."

The teakettle, increasing its volume, shrieked its announcement of hot water. As Patrice adjusted the burner to simmer Cathy said, "Well, you're probably ready to have dinner. I hear the teapot. Please be good to yourself, sweetie. I mean that. Don't be stubborn and courageous."

Patrice's false laughter rippled, but she guessed her sister would not suspect her deceit. "You can be sure I will. I'm learning to be selfish in my old age, Cathy. Besides, people don't die just because they lose something."

"Some do."

"Well, I don't. I've got my work cut out for me in Bridgeport. Wallowing around in self-pity is the last thing I intend to do."

"Masochist."

Smiling between garbled fragments of good-byes and I'll-call-you-tomorrows, Patrice replaced the receiver. Immediately her face hardened into a bleak mask. Was she a masochist, planning to place herself in a grueling limbo? Perhaps. But she had drawn some definite conclusions about her life lately. She wasn't a fool who had to be taught the second time. Life was easier if there were nothing to lose—no husband, no baby. And that's what she intended to want from now on: nothing. Nothing but herself and her work. End of conclusion.

She walked to her bedroom. Though her apartment was an extravagance, everything suited her tastes for quality: the white walls and soft peach carpet, the discreetly restrained accents of glassware and greenery. But since she refused to accept a monthly allowance from her parents, and not a single penny from Justin, she spent a monstrous portion of her salary on rent.

Tall smoked windows faced east from her living room, but now she could only see lights near the beach. Off her bedroom, five floors up, projected a tiny balcony that overflowed with the jungle of her plants. The view from the balcony captured fragments of the famous Boardwalk of Atlantic City. Plus a span of the beach that attracted tourists from all over the country this time of year. By midmorning every day, sunbathers spilled over the sand and dotted the Atlantic coastline like brightly studded flags pinned to a general's topographical map.

Peeling off the slacks and blouse and underthings she had worn her first day back to work, Patrice stepped into a flimsy cotton leotard. She tugged it up over her shoulders and nestled it into place to hug her bare skin.

For the first time since returning from the hospital, she posed before her long mirror to give herself a merciless inspection. Her hair, as she leaned back and shook it free of its usual chignon, gleamed, healthy and full. Her skin was clear and vigorous. Her waist dipped with its usual trimness. And her breasts, though they had lost that first pregnancy fullness, curved as firmly and as high as before. Still she saw nothing that pleased her.

She stared at her hands, crushing her breasts. Would she ever "need a man" like she read about in almost every magazine she picked up? Or heard described in the rest rooms downtown by the office girls? The secretaries told everything: every stolen caress, every pass, every affair. Everyone seemed to be having such sexual *fun* all the time. Everyone except her. Sex had never been fun. With Justin it had been a human sacrifice. She had laid herself down and did what was expected of her, wearily grateful when it was over; it left her feeling like a rejected failure, guilty of some crime she didn't understand at all.

Barefoot, Patrice returned to the kitchen to eat her lonely dinner. She tied the band of a blue denim wraparound skirt about her waist as she walked. Reaching for a cup and saucer, she paused, arms uplifted like a ballerina, and tilted her head to listen. The chime of the doorbell echoed distinctly.

Patrice was so astonished at the sight of Madison Brannen lounging against the wall opposite her front door that she froze. Silhouetted in the doorway, straight and speechless, she still held the cup and saucer. The seconds ticked haplessly by as they gaped at each other like victims standing in stunned awe of a hand grenade with its pin removed.

Madison recovered first and found his voice. He tugged at the scruff of his beard and drawled, "I'm paying a duty call, ma'am."

"I thought duty calls went out of fashion when Atlanta burned, Mr. Brannen," she answered with a miraculous semblance of cheerfulness.

He chuckled. The laugh was rich and deep, and the fine web of lines about his eyes crinkled. "Think of me as Santa Claus, then. I brought you something." From behind his back he withdrew her canvas shoulder bag.

"Oh!" she exclaimed, taking it gratefully.

Her green eyes twinkled luminously. For a fragment of time Madison became lost in them. He stared at them with such interest, she flushed and turned her palm upward in explanation. "I thought I'd lost it the day I was . . . sick. I even applied for a new driver's license."

He made no reply.

Finally she sighed and inanely mumbled "Thank you" again. Stepping aside, she motioned him into the living room.

"You're not supposed to thank Santa Claus," he mused, looking about himself. "You're supposed to take what he gives you because you've been a good girl."

She tossed a reply over her shoulder. "No one has called me good in a long time. Anyway, thank you."

"You did that already." He grinned.

Patrice stilled, her expression uncertain. "Did what?"

"Thanked me."

He put her on edge so! Feeling more and more inept, she stood in the center of the room with her hands pressed together, waiting for him to say something. When he didn't, appearing to be waiting for her to say something, she sighed. "It's been warm for this time of year."

Madison met her eyes with the impact of a fist. His smile was so amused at her skittishness, for a moment she would liked to have slapped his face.

"Yes, it has," he agreed with a touch of mockery.

Despite the scruffiness of his beard Madison Brannen was a strikingly handsome man. His terry shirt, she figured, was fairly expensive for the salary of a construction worker. His denims were creased razor sharp, and his shoes flexed with a soft leather suppleness that didn't come cheaply. Yet his meticulous care, even the studied casualness of his clothes, seemed an afterthought, as if the restrictions of any social custom frustrated him. He gave her the impression of vastly suppressed strength, of the raw outdoors.

When Madison swiveled unexpectedly and caught Patrice sizing him up, his eyes laughed at her.

Patrice instantly flicked her gaze away, then wished she hadn't. Looking away was such an incriminating reaction. To make matters worse, she began doing exactly what she despised. She began to fidget, then to chatter.

"I was fixing myself a bit of dinner." The words tumbled rapidly past her pink lips, one after another. "You won't mind if I finish, will you?"

As Patrice preceded him to the kitchen he followed. "You know, Mr. Brannen, I've been meaning to call you. Several times I've started to sit down and write you out a check for the damage I did to your cycle. Actually, I got out the checkbook, but then I didn't have the slightest idea of how much to write it for." She caught her breath and wished she could hush talking. "And afterward I thought of insurance. Too, I wanted to thank you for going with me to the hospital. After the wreck and all, I would have ex—"

Pausing before the kitchen sink, her back toward him, Patrice leaned heavily against it and gripped the porcelain edge hard. She dropped her head in abashment, something she would have sworn she had outgrown.

"I'm sorry." Her voice sounded small and faraway. "I don't normally do that."

With unruffled ease Madison removed the teakettle and turned off the stove. "You're nervous," he said with infuriating matter-of-factness. Diagnosing was something Patrice generally did to other people, not the other way around. She disliked it enormously.

"Are you always so honest, Mr. Brannen?" Her question glinted with its sharp cutting edge.

His dark eyebrows formed their own question. "Do you always eat alone, Mrs. Harrows?"

She looked about the kitchen, almost as if she must make sure if she was eating alone or not.

"You're not expecting your husband for dinner, I meant," he prompted.

She knew precisely what he meant. The whole apartment was a woman's. It was too small. There was only one of everything that counted, not two.

She stumbled into the lie as if it were the unexpected edge of a rug. "Husband? Oh, I uh . . . Justin is never home for dinner."

Why had she done that? Why had she lied to this man? In the past she had used her separation from Justin as an excuse to ward off potential suitors, for not accepting unwanted dates. But now? And to him? Yet she deliberately smiled her reemphasis of the lie.

"I see," he said gravely, as if she had disappointed him.

Suspecting that he might see through her flimsy pretenses, Patrice quickly took down another cup and saucer and placed it beside hers on a tray. She folded two linen napkins.

"Since you're here, you'll have a cup of tea, won't you?" she invited as graciously as she could. "It's the least I can do to thank you."

"No man who pays duty calls would turn down a cup of tea," he said.

Madison braced one foot on the rung of a chair and curled his fingers leisurely over its back. As she brewed the tea he studied the graceful elegance of her hands. So abruptly quiet did the kitchen grow that every small sound suddenly seemed to thunder: the rustle of the tea, the cozy, intimate clink of the spoon against the rim of the teapot, the fragile tinkle of the top when she settled it into place.

For no good reason—unless it was a conditioned reflex left over from Justin—Patrice's hands began to tremble. Not wanting him to see, she swiftly grabbed up a dish towel. Her customary composure was falling short of its performance level!

But Madison didn't appear to notice. Without inquiring if he could help, he lifted the furiously boiling eggs from the stove. He doused them beneath a stream of cool water.

Such friendly casualness from a man was totally foreign to her. Justin had never done such things, and to see Madison behave more like a husband than Justin ever had was disorienting. She almost blurted out that she had changed her mind, that she wanted him to leave immediately.

"There's no need for you to do that," she protested feebly.

Reaching around him, meaning to remove the pan from his hands, her fingers brushed against his bare forearm. Even if he hadn't prevented her with a twist of his shoulder, she would have snatched back her hand.

"I'm very good at this," he assured her. He thumped one egg with a sharp crack and proceeded to peel it. "Is it all right to ask how you're feeling? After the . . ." Hesitating, he was at a loss of how to finish.

Patrice felt the situation slipping from her control.

"After I lost the baby? It's all right to say it." Her head lifted dauntlessly as she talked. She pasted an illusory, overbright smile on her face. "I'm fine now. I try not to think about it much."

Her show of courage was only that to him: a show. He had seen that pretended valor too many times during the war. He had assumed it himself.

"That's good," he said. "I've always thought that losing a baby, born or unborn, was about the most difficult thing a woman could be asked to bear."

"Having a family must be important to you," she mumbled, not caring if he answered or not.

"I guess it is. I don't have much of a family, actually. My mother's still alive, and a sister. She has a small son I kind of dote on."

If his tone hadn't roughened with such poignant wistfulness Patrice would probably have overlooked his comment. But now she peered at him from beneath her lashes. His black brows blunted over the narrow blade of his nose, as if he was pondering something extremely disturbing.

"His name is Miles," Madison explained. His posture had a certain weariness. "He's six. His mother

. . . well she doesn't always do for him what she—" He coughed lightly before he went on. "Sometimes I think I would do Miles a favor if I adopted him. But then I think I couldn't do that to my own sister."

Patrice didn't think she had taken a single breath. The depth of feeling in the man was extraordinary. One would never guess such responsibilities lay in his heart.

Without looking at her, Madison closed his eyes. His head shook from side to side, and he chuckled. "Miles loves to ride that cycle." The blue eyes snapped with humor suddenly and met the alert green ones watching him. "Miles *used* to love that cycle."

At the reminder Patrice gave a chagrined groan. She stepped to rummage through the refrigerator for a jar of peach preserves. Finding them, plus a chunk of Gouda cheese, she proceeded to hack the cheese into ragged, uneven slivers.

"Family is about all I've got," she told him. "I'm overflowing with family. My sister is married to an assistant to a senator. My mother is involved, to some degree, in every charity and fund drive in the city. And my father?" She flourished the knife at the ceiling with the flair of a fencer. "Daddy opened his first gambling casino about ten years ago. Now, several million dollars later, he's opening another new one. Perhaps you've heard of it. The Atlantis II?"

As she talked Madison was frowning at the mutilated Gouda. "Do you have a grievance against that cheese?"

Patrice peered, wide-eyed, at what she was doing. She picked up a lopsided chunk, which resembled a drooping carrot. Her lips twisted into a puzzled pout.

Madison thought her mouth was absolutely delectable. Without braving a comment, lest he mar the portrait she created, he removed the knife from her fingers and sliced off several paper-thin pieces.

"And your husband?" he inquired cautiously, not looking at her.

His question vaulted out of the blue like a current sparking from a live wire. Startled, Patrice blinked at him. Her jaw slackened, then clamped shut.

"What does your husband do?" Madison calmly repeated the question.

"Justin? Ah, Justin . . ."

As Patrice fumbled with her words she became distracted with the beauty of Madison's hands. His fingers were long and tanned, slightly blunted at their tips. A fine black sheen peppered their backs, across his wrists, to sparsely cover the swell of his forearm. He wore no wedding ring.

"Justin owns the *Telegram*," she blurted out in answer to his question. "Justin owns everything."

"But he doesn't own you, does he, Patrice?"

She knew that Madison was measuring her now, testing her, wondering what the relationship was between Justin and her. She took up the teapot and concentrated on the tea gurgling into the cups.

"No man owns me," she said with quiet bitterness. "No man will ever own me."

Though she didn't turn, she felt Madison's eyes all over her. His male force was filling her kitchen. It was overpowering everything. His large stature was saturating her senses, and his maddening humanity. Then she knew—deep in the womanly part of her intuition—that he wanted her.

The tea ceased pouring, and the silence cried out for relief.

She snapped up her head and turned, startled, as if he had called her name. He was observing her as if he had never seen her before, not blinking or moving a muscle, the knife held motionless in his hand.

"But—" She choked and lifted the fingers of one hand to press against her lips, unable to express herself.

Like some victim caught helplessly in a web, she grew aware of a physical response she had never dreamed, after all these years, that she was capable of feeling. It seeped from the center of her body outward to initiate a pulsing, radiating drive, almost an ache. Her nipples tightened, hurting with a fascinating, frightening pain. It was that sexual sensitivity she had hoped would miraculously descend upon her when she had been married to Justin, that arousal that had constantly eluded her. Now she was being consumed with it! Now, when she had never wanted less to feel it!

Madison took a step toward her, but stopped.

"There!" she exclaimed briskly, suddenly regaining control of herself. Her hand clutched the teapot protectively to her bosom.

"Patrice—"

"And now, Mr. Brannen, if you'll tell me how much money I owe you, I'll write you out a check while you enjoy your tea."

He shrugged, refusing to gratify her by looking away. "I don't know."

"What d'you mean, you don't . . . know?" She could hardly keep her mind on anything except his knowing gaze!

"I just don't. I haven't had an appraiser look at it."

"Well, when will you get one?"

She asked the last words quite rapidly, and Madison, letting his shoulders lower noncommittally, informed her that he wasn't the slightest bit interested in the Kawasaki. He knew what she was feeling, she thought. He knew!

As it finally dawned on Madison that his roving inspection was entirely out of line he jerked his head away and his eyes downward. He reminded himself she was married.

Patrice, stepping away in relief that he had quit scrutinizing her, struggled for short, frantic breaths. From the side of her vision she saw his middle finger thoughtfully stroking his mustache.

"Well, okay," he agreed with some effort. "I'll call an appraiser soon. Then I'll see you."

"You can just call me," she said, dwindling off to nothing.

"That's what I meant."

If she said one more word she would only make matters worse, but she was already speaking. "Or the adjuster could drop me a line himself. Or he could call."

He controlled everything now! With that damned, knowing sobriety!

"It's all right, Patrice," Madison said quietly, understanding. "I'll take care of everything properly. I know you're . . ." He caught his lips between his teeth, then sighed. "That you're married."

"I didn't mean it like that!" she cried distraughtly. "It's just that you—"

Her overreaction shot through the room like the unexpected misfire of a gun. It was too soon to meet a man as compelling as Madison Brannen! She would never be ready to meet a man like him. Realizing what a mistake it all was, she buried her face into her free hand. Her hair swirled madly about her face.

Madison drew his chair away from the table and slumped down onto it. Now he was balanced on its back legs. He pretended to be calm, but the compassion he had felt for her in the ambulance had just compounded itself into something much more male. He had known better than to become emotionally involved with her. Never in his life had he met a more hands-off woman.

He didn't smile. "I seem to be saying all the wrong things to you, don't I? Would you like me to leave?"

"Yes!"

The chair slammed flat to the floor as he started to rise.

"No." Her heavy lashes fluttered. "I'm sorry. How rude of me. Of course you mustn't leave. I—I . . ."

In an unconscious gesture of pain, Madison rubbed one of his legs, but Patrice was so rattled by now that she could do nothing except slide down in her own chair and silently sip her tea. Neither of them seemed capable of carrying on a conversation.

Finally Madison grinned at her, flashing straight white teeth. "Well, here's to good health, Patrice," he said and lifted his cup of tea in a toast.

Calling her by her name was so honest it reminded Patrice of the lie she had just told him. She tried to appear guiltless over the rim of her cup.

He shoved his chair back from the table. "I really ought to be going. I just wanted to return the purse and see how you were doing. I never meant to . . . well, whatever."

Patrice realized, suddenly, that she didn't want him to go. Not like this. Rising with him, she crumpled her napkin beside her plate.

"Are you sure you won't have another cup of tea before you leave?" She retrieved the hefty little teapot from where she had placed it on the stove.

"I really shouldn't," he replied to the questioning arch of her brows. "I wouldn't enjoy walking into my own kitchen and finding a strange man having tea with my wife."

Now he had trapped her into admitting that her relationship with Justin was in trouble. She compounded the lie. "Justin and I make it a habit to not interfere in each other's lives," she replied tonelessly.

"How very civilized." Madison began a loose-jointed amble toward the door as if Justin's habits couldn't be more immaterial to him.

Patrice's intentions were to place the teapot down on the counter behind her and follow Madison to the door. However, she misjudged the edge of the stove as she turned.

Before Madison reached the door a glittering shower of glass sprayed across the floor. Hot tea spattered over her bare legs and dribbled down her ankles in spindly golden rivulets. The top of the teapot, as they both stared at it, skittered across the floor to bump against the wall with a dismal, disheartening clink.

"Oh, dear," she moaned. She couldn't keep from threading her hands through her hair. "Oh, dear, *dear.*" Must she persist in destroying something every time she was around this man?

Madison reacted with the quickness of a man accustomed to emergencies. "It's all right," he reassured as he stepped beside her. He bent with a slight intake of breath. He braced one knee—his less injured one—in the middle of all the broken glass and began gathering the largest pieces into a cupped palm. "Did anyone ever tell you that you're accident-prone, my dear?"

She was in no mood for teasing now. "No one. *I never do this!*" Moist, teary droplets collected on the tops of her cheeks. Having him see her cry would be the last straw. "I'll get a wastebasket."

"Don't move, Patrice!" With the edge of his fingernails, Madison raked the splinters from around her feet. "Not unless you want the soles of your feet to look like a checkerboard."

"I can clean it up."

"I know you can clean it up. Will you please keep still?"

He was so swiftly, so totally in charge, that Patrice meekly submitted. But even as she peered down at the hair curling sensuously on his neck and his jaw that hovered only inches above her knees, she wasn't the least prepared for him to touch her. As he blotted the runnels of tea from her feet with the dish towel she choked in surprised reaction.

His strokes hesitated, then resumed.

"You don't have to . . ." she whispered inadequately.

In the act of blotting her ankle, he paused again.

She suspected he was waiting for her to take a breath. She couldn't. She couldn't move or speak or die. She could only think: *Oh, God, I'm not ready for this! I'll never be ready for this!*

As Madison stooped at her feet his head tipped upward. His very posture—a position which would make most men appear weak—somehow enhanced his virility. He gave her the impression of vital, harnessed strength.

Without looking at the towel, he dropped it beside her feet. The blue of his eyes glistened with a mixture of emotions Patrice couldn't isolate. Very slowly, as she gave a long, fluttering sigh, Madison unfolded himself to stand.

His arms closed about her in a prolonged, suspended motion. She could easily have darted away from him, but she didn't move. As he lifted her free of the treacherous glass Patrice let him hold her tightly against him. Instead of releasing her when he stepped clear, Madison let her slide earthily downward in his arms until her breasts were crushed between them. Her bones fitted neatly against his, and her thoughts—those which were left to her—splintered. She grew intoxicated with the clean, masculine smell of him, their warm breaths mingling, his hard, surging muscles. Her head fell forward to the pillow of his shoulder.

One of Madison's arms shifted below the fullness of her hips. He held her like a child. "Patrice?" he murmured, tilting his head. "A taste?"

From faraway Patrice heard the sound of his voice. She shook her head slowly, denying him.

The tip of his nose lowered to caress the curve of her cheek—silkily, experimentally, as if he expected to be rebuffed. As he peered down at her she looked up. Each of their thoughts concentrated on the mind of the other. Each was half hoping something would stop this because she knew the lie she had told and he had believed it.

"Please?"

Again she shook her head, and again his face touched hers.

"Just . . . a . . . taste," he whispered as his lips tested hers in a series of feathery, wispy kisses. But gradually his lips parted. For a moment his mouth hovered, slanted, clung gently. Then, with a ravaging intensity, which increased to grind hard across hers, his kiss conformed to hers. He devoured her, as if he were suddenly starving for something that drove him, something that had no name.

"Please, no," she begged into the kiss and realized she had only moaned. Already it was too late. His eyes were closed. His lashes furled thickly against the bladed planes of his cheeks. Hers were closing, too, though she didn't mean for them to. She felt her practicality spinning crazily away from her, and she thought, *Please don't kiss me anymore! I don't want to compare you with Justin!* But he didn't stop kissing her. His desire for her was exquisite, and it began draining her strength.

"No!" She choked and kicked for the floor with her feet. "I can't."

Madison took a moment to steady his own destroyed composure as he placed her onto the floor. "But you just did."

Still tasting her in his mouth, he watched her scrub the palms of her hands down her cheeks as if they burned her. Now he understood the paradox of Patrice Harrows that had bothered him from the beginning. She was at tremendous, unbelievable odds with herself, fighting her own feelings, trying to rid herself of pain and sorrow as if one more would break her irreparably. She was, in all sincerity, attempting to live like a machine, devoid of any emotion.

He adjusted his belt and wisely stayed where he was. "Justin Harrows is a fool."

Patrice focused her eyes on him and frowned. "You have no right to say that."

"I have every right. He's hurt you."

She looked away then. "If he has, that's between him and me." Smoothing the rumpled folds of her skirt, she moved past him to the living room. She gave the top of her old-fashioned desk a push, and the top rolled open with a clatter. "You've made a mistake with me, Mr. Brannen."

His voice came unexpectedly from behind her head. "I don't think so."

Patrice took several steps from him. Since she had no answer to his charge, she drew out her checkbook and began filling it out with hesitant strokes of her pen.

Madison impudently read over her shoulder. "Of all people," he said, "you should know how risky it is to write a blank check. What makes you think I won't rob you blind?"

Despite her frayed poise, Patrice smiled, hiding it into her shoulder so he could not see. "You won't cheat me. When the appraiser looks at the Kawasaki, just give me a call so I can fill in my stub. I trust you."

"Then prove it." He chuckled.

She swiveled in her chair and stared hard into his eyes. The blue in his twinkled mischievously. For a second she thought she knew what he must have looked like when he was a boy—devilish, prankish, perpetually happy with himself.

"Go out with me," Madison urged. "Let me take you to dinner. I promise I won't do anything you don't want me to do."

At those last words he assumed a ridiculous gravity. Her smirk was just as capricious. "That's a catch phrase you should have outgrown by now, Mr. Brannen."

Grinning, he kicked at the carpet. "Aw, shucks, ma'am, I'm just a boy at heart. What d'you say? Seafood?"

"I detest seafood."

His eyes flashed to the ceiling in an elaborate agony. Wondering if he had any inkling of how sexy he was,

Patrice allowed herself the luxury of smiling at him. Then she thrust the check at his chest.

Scowling, Madison took it. He folded it in the middle and ran his thumbnail over the crease. When she rose to walk toward the door, pointedly hinting that he leave, he gave her a tiny salute with it.

"Good move, counselor. Now our business will be finished, won't it? A quick thank-you, a kick in the pants and good-bye?"

"No kick in the pants," she protested and narrowed her gaze with a coquettishness that surprised him.

As he wondered what she was like before Justin Harrows had scarred her up she decided that she didn't want him drawing any conclusions about her. Madison Brannen was a compelling man, she warned herself, immensely charming. Men like him could hurt and hurt and hurt.

Before she could reach the door to let him out, the chime interrupted her stride. She stopped still, one arm outstretched, one hand about to grasp the knob. She pivoted to look at him. His brows were as quizzical as hers.

"I don't believe this," she said and jerked open the door.

As Patrice gaped across the open space at Justin Harrows she felt, unreasonable though it was, like a criminal caught in an unlawful act. In the most condemned manner possible she looked toward Madison, hesitated, then looked back at Justin. She couldn't have appeared more guilty of an indiscretion if she had deliberately tried.

"What're you doing here?" she demanded in a strangled voice.

Justin's beautiful, sardonic smile sent a feeling of disaster crawling over Patrice. Her ex-husband caught sight of Madison lounging against the chair she had just vacated. The younger man stiffened noticeably. He sobered, remembering Madison from the hospital.

"The question is, dear wife," he slurred, softly intimate, "what is *he* doing here?"

Like an irate, wronged husband, Justin positioned himself in the center of the room. The door clicked shut behind him. He jammed both fists deep into his pockets and pivoted, scrutinizing them both. He wore an extremely expensive pair of slacks, which pleated becomingly over his slender legs. The soft Dior shirt opened at the throat, and a gold chain gleamed in the mat of blond curls on his chest.

He threw out a thin hand. "Make yourself at home," he invited Madison as if the apartment belonged as much to him as to Patrice.

Patrice stiffened regally. "Now, just a minute."

Like a satisfied cat, Justin smiled. "That's exactly what I told myself that day at the hospital, baby. That's what I told myself when I learned about your pregnancy from *your mother*." He spun hard on his heel, so intent upon nailing Patrice that he failed to notice Madison's wide shoulders settling and his weight shifting in the manner of a man preparing himself to face trouble.

He aimed an accusing finger at Patrice's scarlet face. "What does it take for a man to learn he's going to be a father, hmm? An act of legislature? A bribe? Surely you know I would have given you a few grand to have heard it from your own mouth. I've never been chintzy with you, doll. Now, have I?"

Most of Madison's experience with Patrice had been when she was at her most vulnerable point. Now, when she assumed an implacable calm, he wasn't actually surprised at her dignity; he had just never seen her do it before. Even though he felt like an intruder on this private argument, he didn't excuse himself.

Patrice lifted her chin elegantly. Striking Justin where he was most lethally assailable, she said, "What makes you so sure it was your baby, Justin?"

For a second Justin looked like someone had thrown

ice water in his face. The beautiful smile waned in shock. But even Madison had to admit that the young man recovered himself magnificently. In the batting of an eye his teeth flashed in a smile. He laughed a rich and insulting mirth.

"You?" he gasped, touching his jaw with his finger-tips. "The great Iron Mistress herself. Play around?" He shook his head in droll amusement. "Don't give me that garbage, Patrice. Of all people, I know you too well. You're good at a lot of things, but sex is at the bottom of the list." He made a sound between his teeth and turned his thumb down so that it pointed to the floor. "It goes right off the page, baby."

The tiny sound Patrice made in her throat was the most pathetically courageous thing Madison had ever witnessed. He clenched his fist so tightly his whole body ached with the need to plant his fist in Justin Harrows' face. Daggers of pain shot up his legs.

Justin was shaking his curly head, not caring that Patrice had become drained of all color, that she flailed behind herself for the arm of a chair.

"No, I don't buy that," the man repeated. He flicked his fingers in Madison's general direction.

With deadly blue eyes Madison glared at him. But Justin only simpered. "Well, what d'you say, Mr. . . . well, whoever you are? Has my dear ex-wife shared the wealth, as they say? Or is she the great Iron Mistress with you, too?"

The insult was lost on Madison. In the space of a few tasteless words the entire focus of his thoughts riveted, not on Justin for the cruelty, but on Patrice's horrified expression. Ex-wife? *Ex-wife?* Madison wanted to take Patrice by the shoulders and shake her until she couldn't stand up.

By some intuition Justin sensed that he had ceased being a part of the game, though he still stood on the field. He looked from one to the other as if he searched for some clue of what he should do next.

Madison smiled one of the most frigidly cold smiles Patrice had ever seen. She wanted to go to him and place her hand on his shoulder and apologize. But that was impossible. The glint in his eye warned her he was not a man who would easily forgive dishonesty.

"I begin to see," he told her in a low, cryptic voice.

He took three steps toward her. Then, as if what he did were some meaningful sacred ritual, he meticulously tore her check in half. Then he tore that in half. And that again, and again. Extending his hand between them, he slowly sprinkled the bits of paper like ashes over her feet.

Patrice swallowed down the strangling sob which knotted deep in her throat. She would have given anything to undo this, to erase the disappointed betrayal lurking in the depth of those clear eyes. "I'm—"

"I know!" he snapped.

She had no idea what he meant.

Giving Justin a curt nod, Madison placed his hand on the door and yanked it open as if he would like to have torn it out of the wall. He closed it, not with a slam, but with a controlled rebuke that was somehow very, very sad.

The silence in the room grew physically painful. Justin smiled his sweet, guileless smile.

"Sorry about that," he apologized lightly. "Didn't mean to make him leave. Anyway, what do you say we go out for a drink, Patty girl? For old times' sake. Hell, all that stuff about the baby, I'm not mad about that. You know I don't carry a grudge for very long. I'd even . . ." He shrugged. "Well, I'd forget about all this mess of a divorce. What do you say? Your folks would give just about anything to see us back together again."

His worst mistake was trying to take Patrice into his arms. She didn't bother to fight him. She drew herself erect, stiffly hostile, frigidly cold. He bent his head and kissed her, but it was like kissing a stone. When he looked down at her, his lips curled in a sneer.

"Justin?" she said between her teeth.

"What is it, Iron Mistress?"

"Go to hell."

She left him standing in the center of her living room surrounded by his own wreckage. Running, blinded now with rueful tears, she darted into the bathroom and slammed the door and locked it.

"Go away," she whispered, over and over. "Go away and leave me alone. Go away."

She didn't know when Justin left. For a long time, she sat on the edge of the bathtub, so weary she could hardly look at her wristwatch to see what time it was.

When she finally emerged, the apartment was empty. She despondently made her way to bed, feeling worse than when she had returned from the hospital.

It was better this way, she told herself many times. She would never have gotten up the nerve to make a clean, positive break with Madison Brannen. He was too unlike any man she had ever known. He had kissed her differently than she had ever been kissed before. The man would have embedded himself into her life and destroyed her all over again, for heaven's sake!

Yes, it was definitely better this way. Now, she would cry a few tears before she went to sleep, but at least she was safe from that slow, sweet smile. What a narrow escape! She should be eternally grateful to Justin for ruining everything!

Chapter Four

Adam Wentworth was a small, unassuming man crowned with a head of snow-white hair and possessing a beautifully disarming smile. Though Patrice loved Simon Clayburne and respected him as her father, she truly adored Adam. She teased him and doted on almost everything he did. She had even become fond of Ethel, his wife, who was the exact opposite of Adam in every respect but the smile.

For some reason Patrice had never figured out, Adam had taken her under his legal wing from the first day she had timidly approached him for a job. He spent more time working with her than he had to, certainly more than he spent with any of his other associates. He shared his vast wealth of knowledge until she sometimes felt he suspected his years were numbered, that he wanted to transfer all the years of his stored-up experience into her head before he died.

It was Adam's suggestion that the Remcon and

Bridgeport people have a chance to meet and air their grievances on neutral ground. Patrice had agreed wholeheartedly, as long as she wouldn't have to attend without him. The selected place of the meeting tonight was a small convention hall located four blocks off Atlantic Avenue. Patrice expected frazzled tempers to attend the meeting in abundance. It was the press coverage that took her by surprise.

She stepped into a room that hummed with voices and was filled to overflowing with approximately a hundred people. Behind the last row of seats was a television camera and a light mounted on a tripod. Standing beside the cameraman, a young man waited with a light meter slung about his neck and a clipboard tucked under his arm. On the opposite side of the room, collected in a group that might as well have boasted a press card in their hatbands, stood the vigilant newspaper reporters.

"Oh, dear," she murmured to Adam. They skirted the room to a table on the left side, reserved for the representative of the Bridgeport faction. "This has all the makings of a good brawl, doesn't it?"

Adam chuckled. "You worry too much," he said with his Harvard accent. "That television camera's our best asset. No one likes to make an utter fool of themselves on television."

The sides of Patrice's mouth went impishly down at the corners. She tossed her attaché case onto the long table and snapped it open.

"I'll try to accept that on faith. So far I've not had it proven to me."

Seated at their table were three people from the small upstate town: Paul Wright, a high-school math teacher whose eyesight compelled him to wear distractingly thick glasses; Rawlins Potter, an editor on the Bridgeport newspaper, who was cleaning his fingernails with the clip of his pen; and Susan Harris, a housewife who looked as if she would like to bolt from the room. She smiled halfheartedly as Patrice took the empty chair beside her.

"Quite a crowd, huh?" Susan observed. She smoothed her short frilly haircut and jumpily surveyed the faces dotting the hall.

Patrice returned the smile. "Does that bother you?"

"No, but I wish the television camera was on the other side of the room."

Patrice laughed. "Keep your back straight, your bosom out, and don't look at the camera." She slipped her glasses from a case and adjusted them on her nose. "You'll forget about it in a minute. I only hope something goo—"

In the process of putting on her glasses, Patrice glanced across at the opposite table. The Remcon officials and advisers sat wearing their neat, three-piece suits and fingering their precisely arranged files and notepads. When she froze, her hands still touched her glasses.

Directly across from her, minus the beard and mustache and wearing a suit that had probably come from Fifth Avenue, sat Madison Brannen. His eyes were riveted upon her. He grinned maddeningly.

It was incredible! Swallowing hard, lowering her hands in slow motion, Patrice thrashed about in her head for something to do, something to hold on to until she could collect her wits. She frantically began flipping through a stack of files scattered in her case. She had no inkling of what she was doing.

Susan leaned toward her. "What's the matter?"

"What?" Patrice faced Susan as if she had never seen her or this room before. Then she quickly regained control over herself. Smiling, she adjusted her glasses again. "Nothing. Well, actually I was thinking about a matter I should have investigated a little more thoroughly. That's all."

What in sweet sanity's sake was Madison Brannen

doing seated at a table with the Remcon executives? she wondered wildly. Him, a construction worker! The answer, obviously, was that Madison Brannen wasn't a construction worker at all. He had conveniently forgotten to mention to her that his status with Remcon, Incorporated, was top-level. He had had the nerve to hold her in his arms and kiss her and let her walk into this meeting with no warning whatsoever of who he was. *How dare he insult her so?* She could slap that gorgeous smile right off his handsome, sanctimonious face!

At the exact instant that Madison shoved back his chair and walked behind Robert Sterling and Phil Anthony, Patrice realized he would approach the table where she sat fidgeting. Adam stood quietly beside her right elbow, shuffling through his notes before taking his seat as moderator of the meeting. He was too absorbed to notice the agitation that had pinched her face colorless.

"Can you wait just a minute before you begin?" Patrice struggled to keep the quiver from her voice.

"Certainly, my dear." Adam gave his papers a satisfied thump.

"I have to go to the rest room. I'll be right back."

Waiting until Madison was practically within speaking distance, Patrice hastily rose and glared straight into his eyes. Spinning on her heel, she walked rapidly away.

She didn't escape him as easily as that.

"Mrs. Harrows!" he called after her.

It occurred to Patrice to wonder what she was wearing. She didn't even remember. Glancing downward, she saw the pale yellow two-piece suit, the businesslike blouse, and unobtrusive wedgies. Her hair was styled with its usual severity. If she had dreamed he would be at this meeting, she might have taken a bit more care. The knowledge of that fact irked her immeasureably.

"I thought it was you."

He spoke just behind her head, his inflections so subtly polished that no one but she would perceive the challenge couched there. Heads turned. Eyes of the press averted to them. Patrice had either to face Madison Brannen and play the charade of congeniality or appear offensive and hostile. Her shoulders dropped in defeat.

"Why, Mr. Brannen." She oozed saccharine cordiality. The dazzle of her smile, however, never reached the green of her eyes. "How nice to see you again. How . . . *unexpected.*"

He was as circumspectly guarded as she. "It is I who am surprised."

She continued to smile. "I doubt that. You knew I would be here. I have the distinct impression that you know everything about everything. You probably own the company."

"Well"—he grinned, standing the proper distance away, looking down at her with just the right amount of detachment—"I don't own the company."

The bones ground in Patrice's jaw. At least he could have the good grace to be ashamed for having duped her! When he extended a large, friendly hand, she wanted to throw his pretended gallantries back in his face. But she took his offered hand.

Gazing down at her with the most infuriating amusement, Madison clasped his other hand over hers.

"My grandmother had an old saying," he said.

"One lie leads to another?"

"No. What is sauce for the goose is sauce for the gander."

Patrice irritably snatched her hand free. "It should have been 'Your goose is cooked.'"

He laughed. Heads turned toward them again. "Listen to me, you little clawing kitten."

"I don't listen to liars, Mr. Brannen."

The black brows lifted at the profound irony of that. "Isn't that a classic case of the pot accusing the kettle, love?"

She lifted her chin regally and tossed a brilliant smile at the cameraman. "Why, you're just chock full of old-fashioned sayings, aren't you?" she taunted him. "You shouldn't even be talking to me. It's bad for your image. To say nothing of mine."

She began inching past him, meaning to return to her table.

Madison didn't dare place a hand of restraint on her arm. His determination grated deep in his voice. "I want to talk to you when this thing is finished."

Her glance cut sharply over her shoulder. "That is out of the question."

Around them people were calling to one another, scraping chairs against the floor and climbing over other people's knees to find a seat. Falling into step beside her, Madison stalled for time.

"I'd like to meet the chairman," he said blithely.

Patrice adjusted her glasses with shaking hands. This meeting was going to be much more difficult than she had anticipated. She didn't relish locking horns with the Remcon people now, even though she was dedicated to the people of Bridgeport. It occurred to her to wonder if Madison's whole involvement with her was part of some plan to break her down.

Her reply was caustic. "Do you get everything you want, Mr. Brannen?"

As he chuckled he ran his tongue along the edge of a slightly uneven tooth. "Almost never," he said with considerable honesty. "Why were you born so damned pretty, Patrice?"

Her chin lost an inch of its imperial angle. "Tell a woman she's pretty, and she'll fall at your feet? Is that your strategy? Well, I've heard that one so many times it turns me off."

They were hardly a dozen feet from the table. His voice was low and subdued. "What turns you on then, Miss Brilliant-and-Beautiful, comparing IQs? All right, mine's one hundred forty. Does that qualify to join your club?"

His tense mockery had its desired effect. It chipped through Patrice's veneer. The flush that stained her cheeks was genuine anger, but at least it was honest. His wide shoulders dropped.

"Nothing turns me on," she whispered raggedly. "Don't you remember me, the Great Iron Mistress? What're you trying to prove by all this? That I'm a failure as a woman? All right, I admit it. Patrice Harrows, intelligence quotient one hundred twenty; femininity, subzero. You're smarter than I am and considerably more . . . more sexy. Does that satisfy you?"

"No."

The one thing about Justin Harrows that had been tolerable had been his inability to outwit her in verbal battles. She was a proven expert in that. But though Madison Brannen might not outdistance her in a contest of words, his nerve in outlasting her emotionally was superior. Patrice knew he had come off the victor in this particular skirmish, and in a final effort at dignity, she inclined her head.

"I'll introduce you to Adam," she said. "Come with me."

"Always," he murmured as she stepped past.

"Adam?" Patrice stood so stiffly she looked as if she were in a body cast. "May I introduce Madison Brannen?"

She rushed through the ritual of introducing Adam. The old man's snowy, intuitive brows moved up and down when he discerned the undertones lying just below everything.

"I would tell you what Mr. Brannen's capacity is with

Remcon, sir," she concluded frigidly, "if I were clever enough to know what that is."

Madison shook the older man's hand with delighted enthusiasm. They both passed lighthearted compliments back and forth like a couple of conspiring buddies. Adam said something witty, and Madison laughed. Patrice only cringed at their rapport. How could Adam betray her by liking Madison?

"I'm afraid I'm not with Remcon per se," Madison was explaining as Patrice collected herself enough to notice how impeccably he was dressed. His vest was buttoned trimly about his ribs, revealing a flat stomach above the neat taper of his legs. Now she understood the neatness of Madison's hands. Before, it hadn't been his hands that didn't fit his clothes; his clothes hadn't fit his hands. *This* was the real Madison Brannen.

"My engineers are designing much of the interior of the plant," Madison told the interested attorney. "It's our job to meet the EPA standards from the ground up."

Adam inclined his white head. "That always spares a lot of trouble, young man," he advised sagely. "Meet the requirements."

Madison's eyes drew Patrice into a tangled web of private meanings.

"Trouble is something I always try to avoid, Mr. Wentworth," he agreed earnestly. By a turn of his body, a guarded move, he caused his hand to brush against the side of Patrice's skirt. Involuntarily she caught her breath.

Madison, hearing her wispy protest, didn't blink an eye. "Who needs trouble?" he asked sunnily.

"Exactly right, my boy. Exactly right. Tell me now . . ."

Adam rambled off into a series of elaborate questions regarding technicalities that were totally lost upon Patrice. As she slumped down before her attaché case, as droopy as a discarded rose, Madison shifted his weight imperceptibly until he had maneuvered himself beside her. The clean fragrance of his soap mingled with the woodsy scent of his after-shave. For a moment she thought she hated him for that, for making himself so appealing.

"The Remcon men surely are trying to be friendly, aren't they?" Susan remarked as Madison resumed his seat and Adam gathered up his papers.

Dragging her attention to the woman, Patrice smiled. "Oh, yes. Well, that's all part and parcel of this kind of company. Frankly I trust people more when they're nasty."

Susan laughed, and Patrice turned at the nudge of Adam's hand at her elbow.

"Very perceptive, wouldn't you say?" he said near her ear.

Patrice didn't know what he was talking about.

"The man is brilliant, my dear. And he has an obvious interest in you."

"Oh, but you're wrong, sir—"

The white eyebrows shot upward, and the smile grew indulgent. He placed his gnarled hand over her tight-knitted fingers. "Give an old man a little credit. I went after my own Ethel with the same vigor. You just need to exert a bit of caution, that's all."

If ever Patrice wanted to escape a room, this was the time. Her entire life seemed to be spread out on display. "There is nothing to be cautious about."

He gave her hands a pat. "Well and good. Remcon would scream 'conflict of interests' so quickly it would boggle you. Discretion is a must here."

"I totally agree," she mumbled bleakly.

From across the room Phil Anthony raised a loud question. Patrice lifted her head to find the television camera swing around to focus upon him. The issues were at hand, she thought, and so was her own future.

* * *

During the days after Patrice's return from the hospital she had thoroughly researched the Remcon-Bridgeport conflict. Now, when she made her comments in public, she was concise and well informed. If the Remcon officials had come to the meeting expecting Bridgeport's committee to be conned by flattery or coerced into complying with something they didn't believe in, they soon saw the error of their thinking.

Phil Anthony, after one especially heated attempt to intimidate Patrice, took his seat with a pointed smile of triumph at the television camera. He congratulated himself on the small victory.

Patrice made a motion to Adam Wentworth and, at the same time, inclined her head to the mathematician sitting beside her. When the chairman held up his hand the room quieted.

Aware of Madison's relentless and most annoying observation, Patrice cleared her throat. "I would like to ask Mr. Anthony what his proposal of disposing of chemical waste will cost the company during the next fiscal year."

The expected buzz of human voices occurred before the Remcon attorney could answer the question. Patrice glimpsed the camera swinging around toward her. Irritated, she wished that Madison would stop staring at her legs. During the entire meeting their eyes had met and looked away, met and looked away. She recrossed her legs and knew that his mouth twitched in a smile.

"The engineers could answer that question better than I," Anthony replied, glad to pass the buck to Madison.

Madison paused that one split second too long before answering. He gave the impression, noticeable to anyone, that he wasn't sure he could take the lady attorney's question seriously.

"My estimate is about a million dollars," he said blandly.

"A filtering system is cheaper, Mr. Brannen," she said.

"How do you figure that?"

"This way."

As Patrice presented Madison with a group of figures, an intricate compilation most people would not have had the patience to wade through, the mood in the convention hall changed from factional hostility to serious attention. For the first time during the meeting two forces appeared equally matched.

"The Bridgeport counsel is well informed," Madison congratulated her, "but she has failed to figure past the first fiscal year. Over a period of the next fifteen years . . ."

The pendulum swung to the Remcon committee. The Bridgeport people looked to their attorney with rapt interest to see what her next argument would be. Robert Sterling and his flanking officials shifted in their chairs and watched her with a new respect.

Madison was an expert in his field; there could be no doubt of that. Each time Patrice made a point, pertinent enough to disturb Sterling, Madison only broadened his easy smile. With a drawl he pinned her down, only to find himself pinned down when she rebutted his argument.

Damn him! Patrice thought. In her own mind Remcon, Incorporated, had worn the black hats and the people of Bridgeport the white hats. Now, after Madison injected engineering realities that increased the complexity of the decisions tenfold, *there was no easy solution!*

After two hours, feeling like a child's punching toy, one that kept springing back after every clout, Patrice lined up the edges of her files.

Sighing, she said, "It's my opinion that nothing more can be decided tonight. I would like to see a written report, Mr. Brannen, free of your personal observations, if you don't mind. I want the complete mechanical breakdown of your initial air-purification system, plus provisions for future expansion."

He nodded his dark head. "You'll get it, counselor."

It was the faint emphasis couched in his tone—the pregnant breath of a pause, the inflection—that created the double entendre. Laughter tittered across the room.

Patrice removed her glasses with exaggerated professional aloofness. "All of us eventually do, sir," she replied in a bored tone.

Again there was laughter, but at Madison this time. He grinned wickedly.

All this repartee enthralled the media, but the only thing it really proved was that Madison's team of engineers were not bought and paid for by Remcon. If they violated environmental regulations in their designs for the building, it would be an honest mistake, which left the people of Bridgeport still facing the problem.

Wrestling with clever minds had exhausted everyone. Patrice wanted to go home.

"Well done, my dear," Adam Wentworth congratulated her on his way out the door.

"Thank you, Adam." Patrice didn't expect any more from him, not as chairman of the meeting, not as her boss. He was not one for flattery. He gave her responsibility, let her do her work without the benefit of gushing or nitpicking. She watched him shake a half-dozen hands before he disappeared.

"What do you think, Mrs. Harrows?" Rawlins Potter asked her. He scanned some notes he had made for the newspaper.

"I think Remcon will be careful now," she told the Bridgeport editor. She snapped her case shut with brisk finality.

"You actually believe those money moguls will spend all those millions on pollution controls?" He sounded pessimistic.

Across the room Patrice was half aware of Madison

standing with one hand jammed in his pocket as he talked to Robert Sterling and Phil Anthony. He looked like some virile male model with his jacket pulled aside to reveal the curve of his hip, the flex of a knee. With an errant lock of hair tumbling over his forehead, his profile perfectly delineated, all he needed was the gold French lettering of a man's after-shave printed below him.

Over Anthony's shoulder he caught her looking at him. She quickly turned away, whisking her case from the table. "I didn't say that, Mr. Potter. I think Remcon will get by with anything they can get by with. But they'll have to deceive their engineers to do it."

Once outside, a gust of wind met her on the steps, whipping her skirt to mold the outline of her legs. She futilely tugged it down. Beyond her, across the parking lot, half hidden in the velvet shadows of a maple tree, waited the Ferrari. For once she was grudgingly happy to see it.

The hum of human voices dwindled behind her, then faded altogether. All she could hear as she hurried across the lot was the soft click of her heels on the asphalt and the wind rustling the leaves of the trees. Behind her was the quickened clip of a heavier, more deliberate step.

Patrice glanced over her shoulder. Madison, following her, adjusted his pace. As he strode one hand reached for his knee. Hesitating, breaking his rhythm, he continued advancing toward her without noticing it. It occurred to Patrice that she had seen him make this exact gesture before. Was something wrong?

"I want to see you," he called. A finger pointed at her as he neared.

She knew she couldn't escape him without a hassle. Holding her arms outstretched like an airplane, her case dangling, the wind playing havoc with her skirt, she made one sassy pirouette.

"Look, then," she retorted mockingly. "No one's stopping you."

He swore under his breath, but she still heard it. She smiled at his irritation. That was for baiting her before the television camera, she congratulated herself.

She wrenched open the door to the car and tossed her case onto the front seat. "Are you trying to ruin my ethical reputation on this case?" she asked him as she stooped.

Madison, frowning, stepped up behind her. He leaned an arm on the top of the car and memorized the curve of her hips as she bent.

"Do you always do that?" he said, peering into the backseat.

Patrice nearly stumbled in an attempt to keep from stepping on him as she straightened. She returned the frown.

"Do what?"

"Get into a car parked in the shadows without looking inside first. You trying to get yourself mugged? Or worse?"

Smirking, she braced one fist on her hip. "It's the 'or worse' that always gets me, Madison. Would you say 'or worse' if I were a man?"

Madison sighed as if hitting her were a real possibility. "I can see the inscription on your tombstone. 'Feminist to the battered end.' You're a fresh kid, Patrice. Justin give you the car?"

She jammed a finger beneath the blade of his nose. "You're the fresh kid, I think!"

"So he gave you the car."

"As a matter of fact, he did not."

The wind persisted in dislodging tresses of hair from her chignon in the most fanciful way. She brushed them aside with a gesture that Madison found enormously fascinating.

"You think I'm a snob, don't you, Madison?"

His head tipped back in rich laugher. "Twenty-four carat."

"Well, I'm not."

She stood in the wedge created by the open door of the car, growing more uneasy by the second. As he let his gaze amble over her windswept allure, Madison moved one step closer to her. The wall of his body effectively trapped her.

Not expecting this, especially after their heated exchanges, Patrice's fingers fluttered to the fold of her blouse where its opening framed her throat. She toyed with the button at the bottom of the V. Madison daringly grasped her forefinger as he would have picked up a pencil. Lifting it, he touched the tip of it to the tiny dimple in the center of her chin.

"Prove it, then," he murmured huskily and traced the column of her throat with the point of her own fingernail.

Patrice's whole body grew too warm. *What was he doing?*

"Prove what?" she choked.

She tried to take a deep breath, but she couldn't. Her composure slipped another notch when he drew her fingertip down the smooth hollow between her breasts, over one's curve to pause at the precise center. The feel of her own body responding snapped her out of his spell. Snatching her hand free, she attempted to turn away.

"Have dinner with me."

"I can't."

"Why not?" He systematically broke her down.

"I just can't, Madison! For one thing, I'm so tired I can hardly stand up."

His grin bordered on lewdness. "Let me take you home and put you to bed, then."

She had managed to squeeze past him to the car seat. Now she stopped in midmotion. Straightening, her green eyes snapped with a combination of despair from his chipping away at her and panic because he was succeeding more than he knew.

She threw back her head. "Madison, that's exactly why you wear me out! What do you want? For me to keep behaving like some idiot I don't even recognize?"

Madison was caught in the half shadows of a long, overhanging limb. At this moment she had her first unhindered look at him without the beard. From his tan she could see where it had been. The same tremor shot through her as before; she recognized it this time. The urge to smooth her hand over his jaw, to cup it in the palm of her hand, to feel the tingling roughness of where he had shaved was almost irresistible.

As if he read her thoughts, he sobered.

"I think you know what I want," he warned her softly. "If you don't, you ought to. Unless Justin was more inept than I think he was."

Not having an inkling of where to go from here, Patrice glanced over the parking lot to glimpse Robert Sterling and Phil Anthony walking toward them.

She decided to tell him the truth. "I've been advised that seeing you is an unwise move on my part. I can't help but agree, Madison. If you have anything further to say to me, you can send me a memo at the office. I wish you the best in your work at Remcon. Honestly I do."

With a movement of unbelievable fatigue, she settled herself onto the bucket seat of the car.

Shutting her door, bending down until his face was level with hers, Madison opened his mouth as if he had something important he wished to say.

For a timeless space Patrice wished he would tell her. But he didn't. He merely touched the center of her mouth with a fingertip. He made a kissing motion with his mouth, then gave her a quick, wry smile. He straightened himself and began ambling toward his associates from Remcon.

With a snarl and a muffled meshing of gears, Patrice

left him immersed in the shadows of the tree, watching her drive away.

"There goes one of the best-looking pieces of trouble I ever saw," Anthony joked, inclining his head.

Madison shot the attorney a queer glance. "You thrive on trouble, Anthony?"

The other man measured glances with him, then smiled. "I run from it like leprosy. Which is what you'll do if you're smart."

Robert Sterling cleared his throat. In his meticulous way, he agreed with the legal adviser. "It's best not to stir up talk, don't you think?"

The entire conversation irritated Madison no end. He pasted a diplomatic smile on his face, one he had practiced for years and which held more danger than either of them realized.

"I'm not getting paid to think," he said dryly. "I'm getting paid to do a job that'll keep you two out of court. Good night, gentlemen."

Over the roar of the vacuum cleaner Patrice hardly heard the ring of the doorbell. She flicked the switch to "off" and crossed the room as the machine wailed its final complaint and died.

"Aunt Patty!" Two girlish voices squealed in unison as the door opened and Patrice stood captured within its frame.

From behind the backs of Betty Clayburne and Cathy, two girlish bodies gleefully emerged, wearing shorts and tank tops. Each of them proudly presented a gift-wrapped box topped with a splendid pink bow.

"And the ribbons match the ones in our hair, too," Robin announced. She was the older of the two and took her elder-sister stature very seriously. Both girls vainly rotated their heads to show off the hair bows in question.

"I see, I see," Patrice beamed as she caught her breath. She sent a look toward her mother dressed in a froth of voile and a wide-brimmed hat. "Which ribbons get opened, Robin? Yours or the boxes'?"

"Oh, Aunt Patty," groaned the four-year-old Janie. "*These* are for you. They're the *surprise!*"

Patrice widened her green eyes and made an elaborate production of standing corrected of her error. "Goodness! It's not my birthday, is it?"

"It's an or-di-na-ry day surprise." Janie giggled her mastery over the big word and flashed her aunt the dimple in her cheek.

"Oh, of course." Patrice nodded, motioning them all inside, wishing she had worn something better than faded jeans, an old shirt, and grubby sneakers.

Betty and Cathy laughed at the antics as they herded the girls into the cheerful, compact living room. Cathy kept attempting, unsuccessfully, to lower the volume of her daughters' enthusiasm, and Betty, glancing at Patrice's hair bound up in a checkered turban, only smiled.

Betty's disapproval, though generally offered in fondness, no longer upset Patrice. She wound up the vacuum-cleaner cord and ignored her mother's inspection of cleaning bottles and cans. She devoted her full attention to her nieces and stooped to receive a rousing hug from each.

"Not so loud, girls," Cathy cautioned. "You'll have the fire department up here thinking the place is burning down."

The girls impishly took one of Patrice's hands and, with much giggling and conspiracy, dragged her to a chair and pushed her down into it.

"You sit here, Aunt Patty," Robin commanded with imperial authority. She surveyed the room with somber consideration, then gestured to the chair. "This is the throne. Mother says you're Queen for a Day. You think this is okay, Mother?"

"Patrice?" Betty remarked as she placed her handbag beside the cleaning supplies and began the glove-removal ceremony. "Vacuuming, in the middle of the day? Really, dear, you shouldn't have to do that."

Over the clamor of the girls, Patrice raised her eyebrows meaningfully. "Well, who'd do it, Mother? A magic genie?"

Betty curved her mouth into a lovely elegant pout. "If you lived back in your own home, you'd have a maid to do things like this."

Patrice gave a laughing groan. Though her manner with Betty was lighthearted and charitable, as it almost always was, her message was unquestionably firm. "*This* is my home now, Mother. Justin has his home, I have mine. And a maid would drive me bananas. Well now, Janie, which of these lovely surprises do I open first?"

A heated discussion followed about which gift should be opened before the other. Over the process of arriving at such a monumental decision, Patrice was aware that Betty was roaming about the apartment, probably in amazement that her older daughter would stoop to living in only three rooms and a bath.

Betty telegraphed a visual message across the girls' heads to Cathy: *Poor Patrice, how does she stand it?*

Cathy shot a frown back at her mother in a decidedly clear message: *Please, Mother, don't spoil everything!*

Patrice, catching the gazes of them both, her lips compressing for a fraction of a second, warned them that she wouldn't tolerate any unsolicited advice about her life-style.

The box-opening ceremony turned out to be a gala affair. The vacuuming of the carpet had been a waste of time; soon tissue paper lay in fragments and pieces, and swirls of pink ribbon curled about Patrice's feet. Robin's gift was a long silk scarf in pink and cranberry shades. Janie opened most of her gift herself and eagerly described the heart-shaped pin in detail long before she fished it out of the box.

"Thank you!" Patrice exclaimed, properly impressed. She snatched off her turban to tie her hair back into a heavy swath with the scarf. She pinned the heart to the front of her T-shirt, and they all agreed it was time to migrate to the kitchen to make ice-cream floats.

"You girls may watch cartoons in the living room if you're very careful not to spill," Cathy suggested, eager to settle them down.

Betty, doting grandmother that she was, arranged the girls satisfactorily and returned to the kitchen to sit on a stool as Cathy and Patrice washed up the mess. "Justin came by to see Simon and me the other evening, Patrice," she announced casually, as if she weren't flirting with an explosive.

"Patrice would probably rather not hear that, Mother." Cathy bent to load the dishwasher.

Betty sniffed. "Justin and I remain close friends in spite of all this terrible divorce. I was shocked at the way he looked, Patrice. Really shocked."

Patrice replaced the ice cream in the freezer. "I saw Justin just a few weeks ago, Mother. He looked as beautiful as ever to me."

"Yes, he told me he dropped by."

From the silence that crept across the kitchen, Patrice realized that the subject of Justin's visit had been discussed in advance between her mother and sister. She was sure that telling her about it was Betty's idea, not Cathy's. In the past Cathy had never shown any great love for her ex-husband. Yet, though Cathy might disapprove of Betty's interference in Patrice's affairs, her objections would only go so far. She had never, to Patrice's knowledge, openly defied her mother about anything.

When Patrice closed the door of the refrigerator, she did it with cautious precision. "Justin told you that?"

Rising to shake the coffeepot, Betty fetched herself a

cup. "He still cares for you very much, darling. He begged me to do what I could. Anything to get you to believe how sorry he is that you two're living apart."

"We're not living apart, for pity's sake!" Patrice began to grow exasperated. "We're divorced! There is a difference."

"Still, he was so upset that you had lost the baby, he broke down and wept."

Patrice's eyes flicked to the ceiling in a silent outcry for patience with her mother's attempt to repair the irreparable. "Mother"—she clinched her teeth—"Justin turns on tears like a . . . like a mechanical doll. You can't pay any attention to that."

"I think he still loves you."

Without replying or debating an issue that had never been true, even when they were married, Patrice held a dishrag beneath a stream of running water. She mopped up the countertop, pausing to scrub diligently at some imaginary spot. She rinsed the rag, wrung it out carefully, then folded it neatly across a rack beside the sink. Cathy and Betty watched her apply a dot of hand lotion in the palm of one hand. She was smoothing it in when she walked out of the room.

Cathy grabbed her in the hallway. "Don't pay any attention to mother," she consoled, glancing over her shoulder lest they be overheard.

Patrice grimaced. "I know Mother by now, Cath. How are you and Harold getting along these days?"

Cathy bit her lip. "The truth?" She shrugged. "Harold is so wrapped up in his career, he doesn't know that there is life going on anywhere else on the planet. Honestly, Patrice, if it wouldn't just kill Mother, I'd consider a separation myself. I've about had it."

"It's your life," Patrice replied, knowing full well that Cathy wouldn't risk rocking any boats when it came to Betty Clayburne.

"And that is an old wives' tale. I don't believe a person can do with their life what they want to do.

Look at you." She promptly switched the topic of conversation and smiled. "By the way, I saw a clip of the Bridgeport meeting on the late news. I hardly recognized Madison Brannen. He's a hunk, Patrice."

The warning glare Patrice gave her didn't stop the younger sister. "You talk about starting a new life, you ought to think twice before you let a man like that get away."

"Get away?" Patrice nearly strangled. "What's to get away? Madison Brannen and I have nothing to get away from. Really, Cathy. Sometimes you're as bad as Mother."

Cathy wasn't ruffled. "He isn't married, is he? That would be the luck. The really good ones always are."

Patrice moved toward the sound of the television. "I wouldn't go through that suffering again for any man, Cathy. I'm not a good loser, and that's all I seem to be able to do is lose things. A smart person doesn't keep battering his head against a wall, you know? He walks around it. That's what I'm doing."

By the time everyone left, Patrice was grappling with a very real depression. She felt she had been pressed flat by some giant, living steamroller. Cathy meant well, but even she got in her licks at times.

Shutting the front door, Patrice slumped back against it and held her heart as if she were an escaping heroine in a silent movie. What now? She wasn't in the mood for cleaning anymore; all the energy had drained out of her.

She gathered up her cans and bottles of supplies and dragged herself to the bathroom. She sprayed the mirror and stood criticizing her reflection. She looked terrible. The natural hollows below her cheekbones were gaunt. She had no color at all, and she must have lost ten pounds since she'd come home from the hospital. She tugged off the scarf from the girls and threaded her fingers through her hair.

Why had Cathy brought up the subject of Madison

Brannen? She had just now begun getting through her days without thinking about the man, wondering if he was doing all right. She had been in his arms for such brief seconds, yet even in her nagging pessimism she had recognized something different. That awareness, unfortunately, had not completely gone away.

How had it felt—the moment when his tongue had sought out the hollows of her mouth? His lips had parted and he had drawn in a deep, moaning breath. Then he had kissed her so thoroughly her head had snapped back over his arm.

Oh, God! She couldn't stand here doing this. She had to get out of this apartment, do something, anything! She strode swiftly through the bedroom and glanced at the telephone as if it were a serpent coiled on the table beside her bed. His telephone number blazed across her mind like a glare of flashing neon. Why had she remembered it so easily? Sometimes she couldn't even remember her own.

Would just hearing the sound of his voice be so terribly bad, after all? Talking to him wouldn't mean they were engaged, for heaven's sake! He was probably home, watching the football game on television. But what if there was a fiancée with him, or, God forbid, an ex-wife?

She felt like she was waiting outside her own body as she walked to the telephone and lifted the receiver. She slowly pressed the correct numbers. She lifted the receiver to her ear, but before it could ring she slammed down the receiver and felt as if her lungs would burst.

How immature she was! How like a victim. What she had told Betty Clayburne so often was not true; she didn't like her life the way it was. She hated it. But why wasn't she willing to do something to change it?

She sat down on the edge of the bed and grasped the receiver again. It shook terribly, but she ignored that.

She was a grown, intelligent woman. There was nothing wrong in having a conversation with someone.

"Hel-lo," Madison said in a deep, rumbling drawl.

Patrice closed trembling fingers over the mouthpiece. What a mistake! she thought wildly. What should she do?

Chapter Five

$\mathcal{T}$ hen Madison's voice drifted over the line, Patrice thought of a dozen reasons why calling him was a bad idea, the most pertinent of which was Adam Wentworth's warning. She had legitimate excuses enough— the Kawasaki, the antipollution report. Yet her past with Justin had conditioned her; she expected all conversations with men to turn out dreadfully.

"Hello," he repeated, his voice deep with sternness.

Flinching, Patrice assumed her self-assured cheerfulness, her businesslike efficiency. "Hello, Mr. Brannen," she said brightly. "This is—"

"I know who it is," he interrupted lazily. "Mrs. Patrice Clayburne Harrows, herself."

"What I called about, Mr. Brannen—"

"Or is it only Ms. Patrice Clayburne now? Hmm?"

"That really isn't important. What I called about—"

"I want to get it right this time, dear. No more mistakes with you."

She closed her eyes in bafflement.

The flirtation in Madison's voice was likable and thoroughly reassuring, but the irritated undercurrents were not. She was about to remind him that his deception at Bridgeport was just as premeditated as her own when the melodic fragments of "Georgia" drifted moodily in the background. She promptly forgot about deceptions and why she had called. A vision of Madison reaching for the telephone with one arm, holding a woman in the other, flashed through her mind.

"Did . . . did I interrupt something?" she asked hesitantly. Unconsciously she twisted the telephone cord about her finger.

"You didn't interrupt," he said without elaborating.

"Oh." For some reason her repertoire of conversational niceties seemed dismally lacking. "I thought you might be watching football on television."

He chuckled. "Me? Sitting around the old tube, drinking beer and watching the game with the guys? The stereotype you see in the movies?"

She sighed wearily. "No, Madison. That is one thing I would never call you. If ever there was *not* a stereotype, you're it."

He appeared to be satisfied with that. A definite humor spiced his reply. "As a matter of fact, Patrice, I was lying here on the carpet, staring up at the ceiling and wishing I had something in the refrigerator besides half a bottle of ketchup."

"Thank you for that," she said. It was her turn to smile now.

"For what? For being such a great guy? Or for having ketchup in my refrigerator?"

"For not calling me Patty, silly."

"You mean I'm not a great guy?"

Patrice, choking back a reluctant sound of mirth, ended up coughing into her hand to discreetly cover it up. "Madison, has anyone ever told you that trying to chitchat with you is exasperating?"

"I've been told that a few other things about me are exasperating, but never that."

Her effort to change the subject was not successful. "What I called about, Madison—"

"You're not going to ask me what those things are?" he urged huskily.

Flushing, thinking he had to be the most outrageous and totally self-willed man she'd ever known, Patrice dropped down upon her bed. She pulled her knees up beneath her chin and limberly balanced herself on the bottom of her spine.

"Madison, I know you've gotten the unfortunate impression that I'm a klutz." When he laughed unforgivably, her lips compressed. "But I'm not a big enough fool to ask that loaded question," she went staunchly on. "Now, what I called about is to discuss the check you so theatrically shredded and deposited at my feet."

Madison's teasing ceased abruptly, and his tone assumed an unbrookable firmness. "We can come to some agreement about that another time."

"Now."

"No, Patrice."

"The report, then!" she blurted, irked at his stubbornness. "I've been meaning to speak to you about it, Madison. You know, I asked you weeks ago for a breakdown of antipollution measures. I've never received it. Surely Remcon hasn't decided to get stubborn about it?"

The long pause on the other end of the line could have implied a number of things from him: interest, disappointment, irritation.

"You didn't get it in the mail?" he asked, brazenly trying to sound surprised.

He was playing his old familiar game now, of pretending innocence, then pulling back to see if she would leap to his bait. She imagined herself burying both hands into his thick head of hair and yanking on it with all her might. She emphasized each word with critical distinctness.

"You know I didn't get it, Madison. You—didn't—send—it."

Madison gave a terrible imitation of Humphrey Bogart. "Well, I kept waiting, sweetheart. I thought you'd come by and pick it up. So I could say 'here's lookin' at you, kid.'"

She forced herself not to laugh. "Then you do have it worked up for me. Send it over."

"Now?" he drawled broadly.

"Well, not this very minute. But tomorrow, anyway. By messenger. I need it."

The unsettling period of silence almost refused to end. What was he thinking, this man who flaunted Bill Blass suits one day and roared along the highway on a motorcycle in worn-out jeans and sneakers the next? She heard him draw a lengthy, wistful breath and found she was holding her own.

"Is that all you need, counselor?" he asked with fragilely veiled eroticism.

How adroitly he flirted! She realized grimly that she had foolishly laid down the only two aces she had. "Ah . . . look, Madison, I have to go now. I just wanted to remind you about the report."

"Sure, sure," he said. "Never let a lady down, I always say. Especially if she can sue the pants off you."

"Now what's that supposed to mean?"

"It means, sweetheart," he replied huskily, "that I lie awake at night, fantasizing about you. You have the sweetest mouth, Patrice."

The sound she made was a quick, shocked intake of breath that resembled an *oh!* She had fantasized, too, but up until this minute she had refused to accept that fact. In her half-sleeping moments she had drifted into a netherworld where she didn't want to wander. Over and over she had relived the seconds he held her—the way he had let her slide languidly down his body, the way they had melded together, their bones fitting in that perfect, timeless way. Dreaming about him had been a mistake, though; she had resolved to stop doing it.

"I have to go now," she choked. Her skin was burning, scalding.

"No you don't."

"I do! Really I do."

"Don't hang up!"

She numbly replaced the receiver into its cradle and sat gaping at it, quivering with the same inner tremor as when he had held her in his arms. *You have the sweetest mouth, Patrice.*

"No, no, no!" she whispered.

She ran her fingers through her hair and clasped her head hard. Sliding her hands to her face, she doubled over in a motion of near despair. She wouldn't let it happen!

Throwing herself off the bed, she spun about in a series of unconsciously paced patterns, hugging herself, shivering. "Damn you, Madison Brannen!" she gritted venomously and knew she was swearing at the wrong person. She had called him, not the other way around. Well, now she knew the error of doing that!

Despising the empty misery that overwhelmed her, she wrenched open the bathroom door and began jerking towels and shampoo from a cupboard. She reached inside the shower and irritably yanked on the water. Calling herself a fool, she began stripping off her clothes and flinging them against the wall.

Enough mistakes were compiled on her list, she warned herself. Becoming hung up on Madison Brannen, even in a small way, would be the worst one of all.

Patrice stepped from the shower dripping wet, water streaming off her arms and legs in sleek runnels. Too bad a person couldn't turn himself wrong side out, she thought, and rinse everything away from the inside, start life over fresh and squeaky clean.

After twisting her sopping hair up in the turban of a towel, she dragged on a short terry housecoat. She was about to plug in the blow dryer when the doorbell rang. Good grief! This apartment was Grand Central Station today. If that were her mother again . . .

Madison Brannen, wearing the usual jeans and cotton terry shirt, the predictably deplorable sneakers, stood outside her door holding a brown envelope. For a moment he didn't move and made no attempt whatsoever to explain his presence. He jauntily leaned his shoulder against the jamb of the door, as if he would be contented to settle there for the entire evening.

"I didn't want to keep you waiting," he said, grinning.

Feeling utterly transparent as his gaze roamed over her dishabille, she stepped back, clutching her robe tightly closed.

"Don't run off," he said very softly.

His inspection finally reached her eyes. He moistened his lower lip in a maddening approval of what he saw, detached himself from the door, and stepped blithely forward. He extended the envelope.

"What's this?" she demanded tonelessly. She gaped at the envelope as if it were poisonous.

"What you asked me for. What d'you think?"

"Thank you," she said stupidly and accepted the envelope with a hand that didn't feel remotely connected to her body.

For a moment she remained unmoving. Then, realizing she stood outside her door in her bathrobe, she glanced up and down the hallway and walked back into her apartment. Without being invited, Madison strolled behind her. Only the sound of him shutting the door sent her whirling about to see they were both in the same room, she half naked and he undeniably interested in that fact.

"I'm hungry." He shrugged, as if that were reason enough for his presence. He looked about at the freshly cleaned room. "What have you got to eat?"

Patrice started. "But I didn't—"

"Invite me for dinner?"

Her turbaned towel had come unwound, and she lifted both hands to her head. When he smiled, she realized her posture revealed almost the entire length of her naked legs. Raking her hands down her sides, she let the towel slither abysmally to the floor.

Between flashes of his splendid white smile, Madison picked up the towel. With infuriating slowness he draped it over her shoulder, arranged its folds with bold presumption and stepped back as if he were an artist about to paint her portrait.

"I know you didn't invite me," he said. "That's one of the exasperating things about me I would've told you if you'd asked. What've you got in the kitchen that's good?"

"Nothing, Madison!"

Madison, pretending amusement, wondered if she had any idea of how protective the sight of her made him feel. He doubted it. Without makeup, her hair wet, the weeks of strain since her stay in the hospital had marked her. Her pale beauty had a certain ethereal delicacy about it that pained him. The independent pride in her eyes made him want to capture her face between his hands and kiss her until she clung to him for strength.

"Well"—his fingers gestured lightly at her robe and swept downward to her bare feet as he smiled—"do something about that and we'll go shopping for groceries."

"I explained to you before. It's best if I'm not seen with you."

Madison's eyes narrowed impatiently. "I'll disguise myself with sunglasses. Get dressed."

More than a little astonished at his nerve, Patrice was dumbfounded at herself even more when she said something about needing to go to the market anyway. But the truth was, she got the decided impression that if she didn't do as he told her, Madison wasn't above making a nuisance of himself. Perhaps this is what she had really wanted all along, to be with him, to be relieved, for once, of all her responsibilities and let someone "take over," to at least *think* of herself as someone besides Justin's ex-wife and an almost mother.

She promptly left Madison sitting on her living-room sofa, flipping through a magazine she was positive he didn't even look at.

Patrice's apartment building was located in one of the newer residential districts of Atlantic City. Yet she had never particularly enjoyed shopping in the swanky, streamlined supermarket in the mall near the subdivision. Instead, she always drove a dozen blocks out of her way to a small overcrowded market whose shelves were a disorganized mass of everything from locally made tofu to special stone-ground wheat flour shipped in from Kansas. She liked the friendly familiar faces of the clerks and being smiled at and called by name.

Now she gave Madison directions as he drove, then ended up having to explain her penchant for quaint old neighborhood stores. Madison chuckled, tossing her agreeable glances as he steered his restored forties pickup through early evening traffic.

Patrice, squirming a bit beneath his pointed scrutinies, listened politely. The evening was quite warm. Her pastel-green slacks were cool, but they vividly revealed the lines of her legs as she crossed them. The cotton knit top was sleeveless, perhaps too low cut but comfortable. She had fastened a single gold chain about her neck, and she toyed with it now. Her hair, smoothed back and caught with a clip at the base of her neck, streamed down her back in a thick, gleaming swath.

"You remind me of my mother," he said. "She's been shopping in the same store for the last thirty-five years. She stays with it because Miles can ride over on his bicycle and they know who he is and give him chewing gum and a bottle of pop."

Patrice crinkled her nose delectably. "That's what I've always wanted, Madison, to remind someone of their mother."

Smiling, he was about to explain that he had truly meant it as a compliment of sorts, but she waved him toward a crusty old building across the street. Streetlights brightened the crowded parking lot, and a neon sign with one of its letters shorted out said FRED'S GROCERY.

With some difficulty, Madison discovered a parking place and walked around the front of the pickup and opened her door.

"I like the truck," she complimented him as she stepped lightly onto the antiquated running board.

He laughed. "You said the magic words."

He took her hand to help her down, though it wasn't completely necessary. Again, that startled animal awareness gripped both of them. Madison's grin disappeared, and Patrice slowly pulled her hand from his. The blue of his eyes glinted richly in the darkness.

"Man was born with the ability to dissemble," he muttered presently, which meant, *I would like to make love to you.*

"I-I don't know what you mean," she stammered when she knew exactly what he meant.

Grimacing, he thrust out his jaw slightly. "You see?" Having proved his point, he abruptly changed the subject. "This was Dad's old truck," he explained. "I've been working on it at least ten years."

Patrice's own emotions were unnerving her so badly

she missed a step. She glanced out over the parking lot as if she searched for a safe place to hide from his insistent masculine aura.

Madison smothered a private, satisfied smile. She was weakening. If he had his way, she would belong to him completely.

As Patrice led the way through the doors and selected a shopping cart she paused a moment to gaze up at him. "I hope you're not terribly, terribly hungry," she said, hesitantly apologetic. "I just paid the rent."

He pulled a face at her and wheeled the cart away to begin browsing through the fresh-produce counter.

"I'm buying," he informed her with cool nonchalance.

Speaking softly because everyone in the store knew her, Patrice stepped beside him and removed the tiny peppers from his hand. She tossed them back into the mirrored bin.

Her eyes were green slits of insulted equality. "Pardon me?"

"You heard me."

"Yes, I heard it, but I won't have it. No guest of mine is going to pay for his dinner."

Madison glanced over her shoulder, pausing without a reply. Not a dozen feet away a tiny cherub of a girl stood on tiptoe beside the fresh fruit. She pinched a grape off a bunch and blissfully popped it into her mouth. Patrice followed the direction of Madison's gaze.

"This guest is," he told Patrice, hardly aware of his own words as he continued watching the child.

Patrice might have contested the issue, but at the moment she, too, grew absorbed with the childish fingers fitting about another grape and plucking it off.

"Oh." The child gulped in dismay.

Her second pilfered piece of fruit slipped from between her chubby fingers and rolled haphazardly beneath Madison's shopping cart. With guileless brown eyes she peered at the towering man above her and pondered her predicament. Blinking, she made the decision to crawl under the cart after the now-grubby grape.

Patrice caught her by the cuff of her shorts as she bent. "That one's all dirty, sweetie," she said.

At the sound of a strange voice, the girl stilled. She hastily began scuttling backward. Before anyone could help her, the child's mother poked her head around the end of the shopping aisle and discovered her. Calling, she stepped forward, grabbed the girl's arms and whisked her into the seat of the cart without a word. She threw Patrice a withering glare as she hurried down the aisle.

Patrice didn't move as they disappeared. Presently Madison touched her hand, which lay draped on the cart.

"What?" She blinked misty green eyes at him. "Oh, yes," she said briskly, "the groceries."

Seemingly swept up in a frenzy to finish shopping and escape from the store, she threw herself into selecting everything for a spaghetti supper. She selected lettuce and tomatoes with hardly a glance. And fresh mushrooms, garlic cloves, and Italian bread. She swooped toward the checkout lane so quickly that Madison could hardly grab a bottle of Burgundy wine on the way out.

No one had to strike Madison between the eyes for him to know that her mood had shifted drastically in seconds. He wasn't certain why, except that it concerned the tiny adorable grape thief. He wanted miserably to hold Patrice, to reassure her, to say, *Let me help you.*

Patrice, however, was withdrawn into her own misery. She shot a wary glance at Mrs. Clements, the cashier.

Elaine Clements, a perpetually happy woman whose warmth annoyed everyone—she *adored* everything—

had not only known Patrice for years, but everything she ate and cleaned with as well. She had followed the divorce with Justin, report by report. Now she beamed, her ample bosom swelling beneath her glasses, which hung by a chain about her neck.

"Patrice?" Madison murmured so softly only she could hear. "Are you all right?"

"Yes!" snapped Patrice.

She slammed down a bottle of fresh olive oil with such emphatic brusqueness that Mrs. Clements retrieved her glasses and adjusted them about her ears. Patrice smiled ruefully, toyed with her gold chain, and moved aside to scowl at the rows of chewing gum and razor blades.

"How are you this evening, dearie?" Mrs. Clements' eager smile was actually for Madison—broad and beaming, enormously curious, sizing him up as a marvelous potential suitor for Patrice Harrows and wondering where the girl had found such a fantastic man.

Madison sheepishly returned the smile and finished unloading the shopping cart. He wheeled it away.

"My, my, but that's a fine-looking gentleman." Mrs. Clements hinted flagrantly to be introduced.

Patrice observed Madison as if she had never noticed his appeal before. As he strolled back she inspected the slender height, the slight, fascinating limp that she had intended to ask him about a number of times. His shoulders swung with a grace that bordered on arrogance. He was terribly attractive, wasn't he? Most of the women about her seemed to think the same thing, if their covert stares were any indication.

"I suppose," she admitted grudgingly.

"A new friend?"

Smirking, Patrice shook her head. "Now, Mrs. Clements, are you asking me if I have a man in my life?"

The cash register chattered its figures, clanged cheerfully at her, and spat open its drawer. The woman's gurgling laughter accompanied it. "Would you tell me if you did?"

Patrice forced a half smile. "No, I wouldn't."

"Then I won't ask." She ripped off the receipt as Madison returned and held it out to Patrice.

"I'll take that," Madison said.

Bending over Patrice's shoulder so far that his body folded possessively about hers, he braced himself by placing one spread hand at the curve of her waist. Through the swell of her hips, Patrice felt the strong flex of muscle and bone. His casual manner gave the impression of a long history of touching, that intimacies were an established practice between them, that he was accustomed to buying their groceries.

Patrice stopped short. In amazement she watched him open his wallet.

With eyebrows so high they nearly touched the frosted curls on her forehead, Mrs. Clements threw Patrice a pointedly disapproving look, which said, *So you really do have a new friend. Shame on you for not telling.*

Between the scolding smile of Mrs. Clements and the laughingly amused reply of Madison, Patrice thought she would never get out of the store. She strode determinedly up beside the pickup and began rummaging through her purse as the grocery boy deposited the groceries in the back. With a half-sullen smile, Patrice thanked the young man. She didn't care a whit that he glanced back the second time to watch her climb into the cab.

Madison, however, definitely noticed the admiring youth. When he crawled in beside her and when Patrice shoved some bills into his hand, he slammed one palm down onto the steering wheel.

Patrice swiveled about to face the window. She heard him mutter "Damn!" between his teeth.

"Don't swear at me!" she yelped and thrashed at the

strong hand that snatched her handbag from her lap and crammed the money back into it.

"I ought to paddle your sweet little behind, Patrice," he growled. "Didn't anyone ever teach you good manners?"

She glared at him. In the muted light the contours of Madison's face were beautifully etched, such an ironic contrast to his glowering mood that she mellowed. The fight abruptly dwindled inside her like a sputtering candle. Her words came plaintively, devoid of any self-sympathy.

"I have been taught many things," she said and didn't explain.

But Madison knew what she implied: Justin Harrows, naturally. He shifted himself on the seat, drawing his flexed knee around until it pressed comfortably against her thigh. Patrice's eyes fell to his knee, and she didn't look up as he took a breath to speak.

He clasped her jaw in the palm of her chin and compelled her to look at him.

"Whatever you're afraid of, Patrice," he said with frightening gentleness, "I'm not going to hurt you like he did."

Involuntarily her eyes closed, but he didn't release her face. "I'm not worried about that," she said woodenly. "I would never let a man hurt me again. It was her face."

"Whose face, darling?"

She hadn't really intended to explain anything to Madison; she owed him no inroads into her secret personal feelings, but when he called her *darling*—his desire to understand as sympathetically proffered as if he extended it to her in the palms of his hands—she slumped back against the seat and prayed fervently that she wouldn't cry.

"Her face. The little girl's face when she started crawling after that miserable grape. I frightened her, and I wanted to reach out to her, to calm her or something. But she wasn't mine, and I didn't dare touch her. And then I thought . . ."

"Thought what?" he asked solemnly.

Patrice pulled from his touch and averted her face just enough so that her profile was perfectly sculpted against the night. She spoke as if to herself. "That if I had my own child I could touch it."

She was so valiant in her bristly, wonderful way, so luminously beautiful, so awfully, awfully alone, that Madison damned his own recklessness and drew her into his arms. He folded them about her and tenderly drew her head to the hollow beneath his chin. He balanced his chin on the crown of her head and simply held her because she needed to be held.

Though Patrice remained stiff and unresponsive, she didn't resist his stroking caresses on her back, nor the way his hand paused and formed the shape of her shoulder, then moved upward to cradle the back of her head.

"I have it all worked out for myself," she explained reluctantly. "Some things aren't meant to be. I've come to terms with that. I don't want children anymore. For a moment I just . . . forgot myself."

"That's a bad way to look at it, Patrice."

"Bad or not, that's it."

"What you don't want, you won't miss?" His fingers repeatedly smoothed a shoulder blade.

"I really don't want to talk about this anymore."

Madison made a clucking sound with his tongue. "You're an intelligent woman, Patrice. No, let me finish. If someone else took this attitude, say your sister, you'd tell her that it would get better."

"That's so easy, Madison."

"No, I didn't say it was easy. But it could be eas-i-er if you'd let someone help you."

Her laugh was bitter as she withdrew from his embrace. She sighed and leaned her head far back on the seat and stared at nothing. "I appreciate your concern. Really. I'm not belittling it when I say I would rather do it my way."

Madison saw no sense in battering himself against the wall she had erected about herself. Though he didn't completely understand it, he did respect it. He gave her, instead, a dose of the universal cure-all, humor.

"What you need, ma'am, is a good man to give you a different outlook on things."

The energy of Patrice's recovered self-sufficiency would have intimidated most men. Madison only grinned at her swift flash of resilience and started the pickup. The gears ground, and he backed them off the parking lot.

"And you think you're that man, I suppose?" she said with a healthy smirk.

He laughed. "You should eat my cooking before you decide if I'm what you want."

Idiot! she thought, though with not nearly the bite that she could have. She usually wasn't so quick to confide in people. How had he done that? Drawn her out as he had?

Patrice also wondered, as she busied herself with putting away the groceries, how she had been so foolish as to let herself become transplanted back in the kitchen with Madison Brannen. He was beginning to fit into her private, self-created world too easily. She had unwisely begun to connect his laughter to ridiculous physical things: to the sound of running water, the flip of a light switch, the opening of a door, the smell of brewed tea. Already he knew where everything was. He helped himself to the bathroom, towels, glasses, and now he was prying through her cabinets in search of a proper pan.

Tangling deeper into the snarl of her previous mood at the market, Patrice viciously attacked the cloves of garlic with a knife. The sharp blade slivered the sections expertly until she slammed it down to the cutting board with a clatter.

Madison, in the process of seasoning his "famous Brannen spaghetti sauce," jerked around. "What's the matter? Did you cut yourself?"

Patrice held her hands beneath a stream of running water and scrubbed them as if they would never come clean. "No," she said.

He wondered if she were pretending and stepped beside her. "Let me see."

Without a thought of hostess etiquette, she snatched her hands from his. "I didn't cut myself!" The sound of her own petulance embarrassed her. "I'm sorry. I . . . I just got garlic smell all over me, that's all."

"Really?" His deep voice drew out the word as if it were mockery, but it wasn't mockery at all. He knew she was hurting inside, and that her pride, or whatever it was that tied her up and made her incapable of accepting anything from him, was preventing her from healing.

In spite of Patrice's endeavors to wipe her hands, he captured one of them in his. "Garlic has to be just right, don't you know? Not too much, not too little. Let me see."

Devilishly, Madison drew her fingertips to his nose and sniffed, then pursed his mouth as if this was an exceedingly serious matter. Patrice watched, transfixed, as he touched the tip of his tongue to the end of one of her fingers. He licked his lips like a connoisseur of human flesh and pondered earnestly.

After a moment, he smiled down at her. "Not bad," he announced. "Not bad at all. I could get addicted to that."

For one unguarded instant Patrice's barriers lowered. She laughed out loud in one of the most delightfully charming sounds Madison thought he had ever heard. Yet when she realized that she had once again misplaced her safeguard against his irresistible intimacy, she rotated until her face was hidden. Her shoulders squared themselves, and she jutted her chin femininely, as if she were physically placing herself far beyond him.

Madison didn't hesitate to step around her. He had come too close to chipping through that veneer of fear that encased her, and he reached for her hand. He grasped it once again, this time to turn its palm upward. With utmost care he lifted it to his lips.

When Patrice realized he was about to kiss her hand, she immediately panicked. With a tiny cry, she attempted to retrieve her hand, to shove him away.

Madison was not a man to be easily deterred, and he followed his instincts. Against her will, he kissed the palm lightly, once, then again with a whisper that Patrice thought was her name.

"Please," she groaned. She cleared her throat in an effort to regain her balance. "Madison . . ."

He kissed her palm again, but not nearly so briefly, or so logically, this time. His lips ceased their teasing now, and his hand moved to the small of her back. With the skill of an artist's brush upon canvas, he drew a nibbling, tingling trail over the bones of her wrist.

"You always smell so good," he murmured.

"There're things about me you don't know." Her whisper broke. He was destroying the barrier of her self-preservation. "Inside me, Madison. I'm not like other women."

His free hand was groping behind him. Patrice didn't perceive what he was doing, except that he made some adjustment on the stove, hardly glancing at it. As he did she saw her chance to break the hypnotizing spell that was filtering through the room.

She took a step away from him, but he only matched her step with one of his own.

"This has been coming for a long time, my sweet," he told her. "A long, long time."

"Not so long. I don't know you!"

"Well, I know you and it's enough."

She struck at the space between them as he stalked her backward.

"No!" Her right hand pressed against her temple as if it suddenly pained her. "I've worked hard to get myself straightened out again, Madison. I've done some terrible things, made some stupid mistakes. I don't want to make any more."

The solidity of the wall pressed against her back, invincibly, incontestably. Her arms inevitably spread out from her sides, as if she could somehow call upon the gods and force the structure to give way.

"You can't go any further," Madison warned her quietly. "You can't go through that wall, Patrice, and you can't escape me. I'm here, and I care about you. God knows why, because you don't make it easy. And you want me to care. You just can't admit it. You need me, sweetheart."

She shook her head and examined her own feet. "I don't need anyone."

Madison didn't touch her. He towered over her and braced one muscular arm on each side of her head, so near that she couldn't even turn from side to side. But except for his breath, which fell warmly on her cheeks, he didn't touch her. He spoke as if he had thought about what he was going to say for a long time.

"You're no different from the rest of us, Patrice. Some people live all their lives for this and never feel it. Some people would die for it. Men I've known have left it behind when they went to Nam and prayed they would just live long enough to come back to it."

Patrice gulped a huge breath. "I don't know what you're talking about."

He bent his head so that he was murmuring against the smooth, subdued tresses of hair. "Yes, you do. You might've never felt it with Justin before. You probably haven't, because if you had you'd still be married to him. But you know."

For all her intelligence and skill and the excellence of

the facade she presented to the outside world, at this moment Patrice felt like a newborn babe. How had he managed to get so far ahead of her in just a few years?

When her face tilted upward, almost level with his, her honesty was written in her eyes.

"I can't let myself think about that, Madison. I swear, I can't go through any of that nightmare again, the hoping, the disappointment, the facing it after it's all over." Her words twisted with unshed tears. "I'm sorry. I don't mean to hurt you."

When Madison walked out of the room, Patrice didn't follow him. She was certain he would leave now. She *had* hurt him, in spite of not wanting to. At this point she was so confused she didn't know if she cared. Yes! Yes, she cared, but she wouldn't go after him. If she went after him, she would be doing exactly what she had promised herself she would never do.

For at least ten minutes she sat at the tiny table staring at her hands and her fingernails. After giving Madison a reasonable time to be far away, she finally dragged herself into the living room.

The room was almost dark, with only one small lamp burning. Madison stood before the windows, the drapes still open, and stared at the blackness of the sky. His feet were spread apart, exposing the tapered length of his legs, his cleanly cut hips, and he had slipped his hands into his back pockets, palms out. Patrice was at a complete loss.

Without turning, he said, "I couldn't go."

She stepped beside him, and for several silent minutes they stared down at the lights of the city below. Madison presently shifted his weight.

"Please try to understand," she said quickly before she could change her mind.

He cut her off. "I wouldn't put any strings on you. I know what you're going through."

She moved away from him, yet she sensed him turning to look at her.

"Do you?" she cried, lacing her hands, twisting them. In a wide theatrical gesture, she whirled around and threw out her arm. "Look at you! So . . . so in control of your life. What you want, you take. When you want to go, you go. Well, it's not like that with me. All my life I've done what people have told me to. That's over now. I have to survive, my own way."

In a flicker of seconds Madison towered over her. The muscle in his jaw flexed over and over. His fingers closed about her shoulders and bit deeply. Patrice winced, for he hurt her, but the look on his face dared her to ignore him.

"Listen to me!" he gritted out the words. "You don't have any idea of what survival means! Wait till you crawl on your hands and knees in a stinking hellhole and wonder every minute if that artillery will find you. Wait until you see nice, gentle men with half their bodies blown away. Then you talk to me of survival, my darling. Maybe then I'll listen."

In his intensity his grip had become excruciating. She writhed beneath it. He released her, but she had the feeling it was not because of her pain.

"I lay in a hospital bed for six months," he tonelessly explained. "And then, after they drilled holes in my knees and put metal inside me, they made me walk." The blue of his eyes darkened to a slate-gray with memories. "You talk about being afraid to try again. . . . I knew no matter how good I got it would never be the same. I was afraid. I hated everything."

Patrice's jaw slackened. When he turned and walked away, her embarrassment was scalding and petty. This time she watched him with a knowledge she had not had before. How many times had she seen him run the tips of his fingers down the side of his leg? How many times had she been so submerged in her own pain that she brushed this image aside?

As he stood with his weight shifted to his better leg she realized she couldn't begin to comprehend the agony he had suffered. An enormous wave of compassion swept over her, like nothing she had felt since she had grieved for the life of her child. Forgetting a thing like pride, she moved to stand beside him. Slowly she knelt. Thinking that she was a fool, she closed her arms about the poor legs that had cost him so much.

"I'm so sorry," she whispered and buried her face against them. "Please forgive me."

Madison bent beside her, detaching her arms as he lowered himself. "Ah, Patrice, I didn't mean to come down on you like that."

He smoothed back her escaping strands of hair, and Patrice lifted her face, her cheeks damp with empathy.

"I'm doing all right," he reassured her. "I've learned how to live with it. That's what you have to do, darling. So a man hurt you and you lost a baby. Start over. We all do it."

Though he kept her face upturned, she lowered her eyes to the thick plush carpet. Her fingertips buried deeply into it, and she twisted a thread as she wrestled with her words. "I'm working it out. I'm starting to heal."

"Let me help you."

She shook her head. "I have to do it myself."

"I'm not Justin Harrows, Patrice. I won't ask for sacrifices. I won't take from you. Look at me."

She obeyed him. Gaunt lines of concern engraved the sides of his mouth. Now that she knew to look for it, she could read the war in his handsome face. Her lips parted as he, too, devoured her with his eyes.

"Just let me hold you," he pleaded hoarsely. "The only time I ever held you was when you were unconscious. Let me hold you, Patrice."

What could she say to such a question? She wanted desperately to be held, but only that. Could he understand?

Patrice placed the palms of her hands firmly on his chest. She could feel the strong rhythm of his heartbeat. At her touch, an expression of satisfaction flickered across his features. In the process of letting him draw her into the haven of his arms, Patrice shifted herself and he, swiveling on his heel, cradled her shoulder in the hollow of his arm. Slowly, by a process that she wasn't actually certain of, he drew her down to the softness of the carpet.

The drapes were open. Beyond the dark locks of his hair the stars twinkled, distant and discreet. She had to straighten her legs. Immediately he covered her waist with a bent knee. Timidly Patrice lowered her hand to the flex of his knee. Her fingers searched out the network of scars beneath the denim like a blind person connected to reality through a system of braille dots and dashes.

He was looking down at her, tracing the arch of her eyebrows with his fingertips. When she touched him as she did, he hid his face in her hair and moaned.

"Does it hurt?" she choked, fearful now and removing her hand.

As Madison groped for her hand his arms brought her nearer so that her breasts pressed wonderfully against his chest. He braced his weight on an elbow and his face hovered just above hers. In the dim light his teeth sparkled whitely as he drew the unsuspecting hand down between them. With a slight thrust of his hips he pinned it very low, very intimately.

Patrice drew a wisp of a breath, but his slow, sentient rhythm paralyzed her.

"Not nearly as much as other things," he mumbled thickly and groped for the alluring honey of her mouth.

Neither of them meant for anything to flame out of control. In a completely separate part of Patrice's mind she warned herself that Madison must be made to understand; a few kisses were all she could surrender to him. After this one last kiss she would tell him so.

But Madison's kisses never ended. One slipped sweetly into another until she could hardly breathe.

Whimpering, moving, turning, clinging, she slid her hands beneath his shirt. His flesh seemed to blister her hands unbearably, so she reached instead for the back of his head. She threaded her fingers through the crisp, furling hair.

"Oh, Madison," she begged him. "Don't do this to me."

Madison cast off his caution along with the shirt he flung from himself. He pulled himself full-length upon her, wishing that he could take her into his own flesh and bones.

"Oh, love," he breathed, inflamed by the innocent caress of her palms, "trust me, trust me."

It was too late. The fire crept out of its preordained bounds, and Patrice knew the first moment of panic when Madison's fingers found the zipper of her slacks. She fought his hands, not in teasing, not in coyness.

"No, Madison, I don't want it, I swear."

Even as she protested, her hips moved in an unconscious, undulating need for him to love her. Madison didn't think she knew what she wanted. Her fear, he understood. He pressed his lips against the shell of her ear and talked to her—soft persuasions that didn't deter the skill of his hands as he removed her clothes.

Patrice grappled for a sanity that deserted her. She would pay for this folly! But she couldn't seem to stop those hands that slipped so silkily between her legs, searching for, discovering, a readiness of passion that horrified her. She tensed her knees, denying him.

"Don't do that," he whispered and persisted until he buried his knee between the vise of hers. "Let me tell you something."

"No," she choked.

His mouth pressed against the slope of her throat. "No man can love you like I will. No one will care as much. Believe that."

"You're not listening to me."

"I *am* listening, love," he said as his fingers invaded

the one thing she was trying to prevent him from taking. "I swear to you I'm listening."

"I'm scared!" she cried into his kiss, arching upward against the systematic seduction he was plying. "Oh, Madison, I can't stop you. Help me."

"In the only way I know," he promised as he conformed, with extreme care, to the way she was made for him.

Chapter Six

*N*ot since she was a child could Patrice remember weeping as bitterly as she did now. Even when it was all over, when Madison cradled her in his arms before the darkened window, when he kissed her eyes and murmured that everything was all right, it didn't help. She clung to him. She buried her face into his chest and shuddered with heartbroken sobs.

He had been so tender, so wonderful, so careful. Still, nothing had changed. She had failed. She had disappointed him and she had appalled herself.

"Justin was right," she mourned against his chest. "In my mind I've always thought he was wrong, but I'm everything he says I am. I'm a failure. I'm incapable."

"Hush, love." Madison tucked his chin low and tried, as best he could, to wipe away her agitated tears. He kissed the quivering lips. "You have nothing to be sorry for. And there's nothing wrong with you. You've been told it's your fault for so long, you're beginning to believe your own lies. We'll work it out."

Patrice shook her head and swiped at the flood of tears. "I don't want to work anything out. I'm tired of battering my head against something that never yields. I'm just so . . . tired."

Madison forced himself to leave her long enough to dress. Even though he was more certain than ever that he should have made the attempt with her, he despised himself. He even knew why the failure weighed on him so ponderously; he was falling blindly, irrevocably in love with Patrice Harrows.

He zipped his jeans and found his shoes and gathered her things from off the floor. Patrice sat on the couch in his shirt, shivering. For several minutes he moved idly about, giving her time to compose herself. *Damn Justin Harrows!* he swore as he covertly observed her smooth her hair, settle her shoulders in a sad, stoic manner. Damn him! The wretch deserved to be hamstrung.

"Come on, sweetheart," he encouraged into the flurry of her hair. He grasped her hands and pulled her up. "Let me help you to bed. Then I'm going to bring you something to eat. And a big glass of wine."

Patrice glanced about the room whose complexion had changed now. All her plants, the furnishings, the quietness would remind her of the woman who wasn't quite a woman. They would never let her forget the disaster of this night.

At considerable cost, equilibrium slowly settled upon them. Then Patrice began to be realistic, to systematically count the mistakes she had made. What a fool she was! When it came to men, the giggling secretaries downtown had more sophistication than she did. If she were inclined to gossip, which she was not, she could just hear what she would have to report: a perfectly splendid man had tried to make love to her, and she had snapped. She had frozen up so badly that she'd covered her face with her hands and pleaded for him to stop.

"I don't want anything to eat." She shook her head. "I think I'll go to bed, Madison. You don't mind, do you? I hate myself pretty much right now."

Madison scooped her up in his arms, despite the cost to his knees. He hugged her to his chest. "I insist, but I also insist that you don't spend this night alone."

From her cradle in his arms, Patrice's head lifted. She blinked spiky, tear-studded lashes at him. "I'm sorry—"

"I'm sleeping on the couch, Patrice. You might need me."

Patrice shoved futilely against his waist, protest written all over her.

"There's not a whole lot you can do about it"—he settled the matter—"so save what strength you have. What do you think I am, a heel? Ravish a lady, then leave her? No way."

"You shouldn't—"

"I shouldn't do a lot of things," he retorted, grimly vexed with himself, "but that doesn't seem to keep me from doing them."

The combination of a glass of Burgundy while Madison sat on the foot of her bed, the coolness of the sheets, and the knowledge that someone would be in the next room was a powerful sedative. Patrice wearily buried her cheek into the pillow. She wouldn't try to solve the puzzle of herself tonight. She couldn't.

The last thing she remembered as she slowly unwound was the look on Betty Clayburne's face if she knew that Madison Brannen was ensconced on the living-room couch with hardly a protest from her own willful daughter.

Patrice guessed, when her eyes flew wide to find a pitch-black room, that it was in the wee hours of the morning. Oh, misery! This was what she got for going to bed at such an early hour.

"Get out!"

She bolted upright. She knew immediately what had waked her up. Madison! For a second she had forgotten he was on her couch. Hurling herself out of bed, she found her robe and belted it securely about her without turning on a bedside light. She tipped up the tiny clock beside the telephone. Two-thirty.

"No. No!"

Patrice's eyes flared with alarm, not about Madison, but at the thoughts of what could be happening outside her bedroom door. Skittering across the room on her tiptoes, she furtively held her breath lest the door make a sound. She opened it only enough to see through.

Total silence. And then the muffled sound of Madison moving as he slept.

He shifted restlessly on the couch, his arm flinging out and dropping over the side to scrape the carpet. Accustomed to the darkness now, Patrice could discern his long irregular shape beneath the sheet.

"Oh, God," he muttered, his knee coming up, his head twisting. "God, don't . . . no!"

He moaned softly as he dreamed. What grotesque tortures flashed through his subconscious to make him suffer so? Vietnam? Of course, he was having a nightmare of the war.

Like a wraith, Patrice moved to stand over him. Uncertain of how to relate to this man with whom she shared so much, she knew she couldn't leave him. She decided to wait beside him until the nightmare had spent itself. She sank to the floor near his head.

But the agony of his dream didn't abate. Madison's face grew gaunt as he relived some horrible panorama. His arm thrashed out, striking Patrice a blow on the shoulder, which nearly bowled her over. She gasped, amazed at his strength. What should she do? Should she wake him?

"God!" He was nearly weeping now, nearly choking.

"Don't let me die!" His head turned from side to side as he gritted the words "won't die" over and over again.

By now Patrice was suffering nearly as much as he was. She reached out to smooth his forehead, thinking it would calm him, even in slumber. But he only struck her hand away and continued groaning his determination not to die.

Acting on instinct now, Patrice wrapped her arms about his shoulders. If he hit her, he'd just have to hit her. "Madison? Madison!"

As best she could, she slipped herself beneath him on the couch and drew his head into her lap, holding him maternally against her breast, rocking him like an infant child, crooning to him.

"It's all right, Madison. I'm here. It's all right."

As Madison's consciousness drifted up from his own private hell he draped a heavy arm across her shoulder. Instinctively he turned his face into the disarrayed folds of her robe.

Patrice's breasts were nearly bared from the struggle to handle such a large man. The prickly stubble of his new growth of beard scraped the tenderness of her abdomen through the film of nylon she wore.

He was waking. He moaned an incoherent mumble and begged her, "Don't let them take my legs." He crushed her back against the cushions with the sheer force of his weight.

Patrice thought she would shatter at the desolation of his entreaty.

"It's me, darling," she whispered and kissed the damp forehead, plucking the clinging wisps of hair and smoothing them back. "It's Patrice, Madison. Wake up. You've been dreaming."

She peered down at his handsome head nestled in her arms, at the curve of his mouth hovering against the tip of one breast. In his grogginess he stirred, and the nuzzle of his jaw unexpectedly aroused the tiny nipple. To Patrice's astonishment it leaped painfully to life. A current of raw electricity raced along the path of her nerves, shocking her to acute awareness all over. For one breathless moment she feared she would suffocate.

As he roused, Patrice's fingers trembled over the swelling curve of her own breast, knowing that only a slight shift of her shoulder would send the gown slithering aside. Then nothing would lie between the cleverness of his mouth and that part of her that was throbbing unbearably. She didn't know if she dared do such a thing. What would he think?

Deploring her lack of expertise in such a sensual matter, she slowly slid the nylon aside. The strap slipped down her arm. Her shoulder moved the necessary inch. Then nothing prevented the yearning flesh from thrusting brazenly against his lips. She held her breath, trembling with suspense, miserable with wanting, not knowing what to do and knowing she must do *something*.

When Madison realized what was happening to him he blinked. He moaned a sound that was almost as agonized as before. Not questioning what heaven-sent blessing had befallen him, he shaped his palm about the curve and drew the small, quivering nipple between his teeth.

Groaning, Patrice slumped back against the couch. Her head lolled back in the throes of the sheerest ecstasy she had ever known. In a motion that seemed to her to be completely wanton, she nestled his head against her, whimpering his name.

Madison came fully awake.

"I never meant . . ." she tried to explain.

Yet she shifted in a restless quest beneath him. Fitfully she caressed his hair, his arms. And when his mouth sought the other, the twin delight she was too dazed to offer or deny, she ceased trying to tell him anything.

Even through the haze of passion, Madison recognized the crisis of the moment. With the unselfishness of new love he cautiously maneuvered her beneath him. He felt the willing surrender of her thighs. Then he abruptly found himself at a loss. Sensing his reluctance to hurt her again, Patrice did the only thing she knew to do. She reached for him and guided him to a place of reckoning, which, at this moment, she didn't entirely understand herself.

Madison didn't hesitate again. He groped for her mouth as eagerly as she gave it. With a groan that seemed the epitome of a lifetime of searching, he filled her with himself. And for a time the risks felt as nothing.

"Justin Harrows is a liar," Madison muttered much later. "A liar as well as a fool."

They both lay tangled together, half on, half off the couch, glowing in the moist aftermath of languid explorations and a gradually evolving trust. Patrice could hardly talk above a whimper. One of her hands rested intimately upon the curve of his hip, the other over her own eyes.

"Why d'you say that?" she mumbled.

Pulling himself up on an elbow and arranging her dampened veil of hair between them, he chuckled. "If ever there was not an Iron Mistress, my dear, it's you. More like marshmallows and whipped cream and such."

"You're a greedy man."

"Granted. More than you think. Marry me, Patrice."

The three words fell with the unanticipated weight of iron—red-hot, cast into a smithy's vat to hiss and steam and make one sweat from the drive of its heat. Patrice stirred weakly, unable to believe he was serious.

"Madison, you have to know—"

He settled himself firmly on the floor, rolled on his back, and stared into the darkness. "I know . . . I know I love you. God, I love you. What else can I say except 'marry me'?"

With a sinking sensation, as keenly defined as the triumph she had just experienced, Patrice dragged the sheet over her shoulders and turned so that her back was toward him.

"Of all people, you should understand why I can't commit myself to any man, Madison. I just escaped from a terrible marriage. I'm not ready to even consider such a step. I'm not sure I'll ever be ready."

"That's a cop-out."

A warning of danger tightened the muscles about her spine. "It's the wisdom of one who's held her hand to a white-hot stove for three years and finally jerked it away. Don't play tug-of-war games with me."

Moving near her knees, leaning on them as a support, Madison studied the serious expression on her face. Patrice didn't object; she simply waited for him to state his case as coolly as if she were in a court of law.

Madison averted his head and scraped his stubble with a free hand. He moistened his lips.

"Have you always sold yourself so short? Don't answer that question. I figure you cut yourself down only in one area—love. What did you feel when you held me? I could feel your fingernails cutting into my back, Patrice. What was going on in your head all that time?"

She wanted to look away because of the deep personal intimacy of his probe. But if she didn't face him now, she really would be copping out.

She drew a long breath. "I'm not so different from anyone else in the world, Madison. I have a pretty good idea of the good things between a man and a woman. But knowing them, even wanting them, doesn't mean I can make a man happy."

"You make me happy."

"But you're . . ."

He scrutinized her; he held his breath to see what she would say. "Go on. I'm what? Undiscriminating?"

"How can you say that? You're the most discriminating man I know."

"Then tell me what I am."

She lowered her forehead to her fingertips; she was the last woman on earth to discuss these delicate matters.

"You're a man who cares, Madison. Perhaps too much. You stumble upon a woman who's never had much satisfaction out of life and it's like a . . . a challenge."

"Oh, hell, Patrice!"

She grabbed his head between her hands as he jerked away. "Please. Please, no. It was wonderful. You were wonderful. I'm the one with the problem."

Madison heaved himself from the floor and positioned himself on the divan beside her. One leg automatically moved across both of hers. He braced one arm on the opposite side of her until his face was directly before hers.

"Your only problem is that you've been too gullible, counselor. You believe what some idiot, forgive me, has told you without once stopping to ask yourself if it's really true. If it were anyone else, you wouldn't accept something like that without question."

"That's not fair. It wasn't all Justin's fault. I was never able to . . . to do any of the things a woman can do to . . . Do you know what I'm saying?"

He nodded, then grinned with boyish pleasure. "I'm glad you couldn't. I want you to do them only to me."

"Madison!'

"Well, okay. But the difference between Justin and me is that I don't expect what you can't do. I accept you the way you are. Physical touching is only part of it, darling. Without the other, the respect, the head trip, the words, whatever, the physical is never enough. Like

117

bumping into a woman at the mall and thinking how pretty she is, then going on and never giving her another thought."

Patrice could hardly argue with his generosity of himself. She wasn't accustomed to it. "I would short-change you, Madison."

Leaning backward a bit, drawing her into the trap of his arms, Madison talked over the top of her head.

"Patrice, you're a bottle of really good wine. Right now you're aging, mellowing to perfection. Once you let someone truly open you up to what you are, when the time is right, you'll go down so-o-o easy. Trust me on that one. Let me be the one."

Patrice couldn't help but smile at his analogy. "Will I sparkle, Madison?" she teased.

Her coquettishness inflamed him. With very little trouble he lay her down and pulled his length upon her. He balanced himself on the palms of his hands. As his knee bargained with hers, demanding an entry, his mouth lowered.

"Ah, love," he groaned, "you're vintage stuff. Don't you know how you go to my head?"

His kiss was only a breath away. He was more than ready to love her again, insistent and straining against her.

"Make me drunk, Patrice," he begged her, touching her lips, pulling away, touching them again. The sheet was a pale cloud on the floor. "Make me drunk again and don't wake me up until it's morning."

Patrice awoke in her own rumpled bed. The memory of how she got there was as hazy and gray as the dawn that flirted around the edge of the room. The quietness, as she rubbed her eyes, was not the peaceful silence of rest but the stark void of emptiness.

Madison had gone. And that, coupled with what they had done, seemed a betrayal in the cold light of day. An adult act, a disillusioned act, she labeled their night together, but it was still a betrayal of the boundaries of protection she had set for herself.

Refusing to allow herself the luxury of self-hatred now that it was done, however, Patrice dragged herself to her feet. She was on her weary way to the shower when the telephone purred. Her anger rekindled like an exploding ember banked in a fire.

How predictable a pattern! Now she would hope it was Madison calling. Now she would be numb with disappointment if it wasn't. He had scooped her up in his lover's net quickly, hadn't he?

She answered on the fourth ring.

"Patrice? Are you there or not?"

Something inside her slipped into focus. The tension melted from her posture and she coughed lightly. "I'm deciding."

She heard his sigh of relief and wondered what he had expected. What had *she* expected?

He yawned. "Did you just get up?"

"Yes. When did you leave?"

"Early. Something wore me out. I feel like an old man."

Braving a laugh, Patrice lowered herself to the edge of the bed. Had she been wrong? Was it remotely possible she would not be hurt over this?

"What plans do you have for the weekend?" he asked.

"I was going to clean house."

"Your house is spotless. I want you to go somewhere with me."

"Where?"

He paused. "Just . . . somewhere. I'll pick you up in thirty minutes."

Madison drove them seventy-five miles. Most of the time Patrice sat primly, as primly as one could sit in the presence of one's lover of an entire night, and thought Madison was obscenely cheerful. With his lazy lashes and beautiful hands and expensive shoes he seemed importantly pleased with himself. She flicked her finger at a wrinkle in her crisp linen skirt, then repeatedly smoothed at the seam.

"Madison," she said with much difficulty, "there's something you should know."

He lifted his dark brows at her. "You once told me I knew everything about everything. Changed your mind?"

She glared at him and pressed doggedly on. "This is one thing even *you* don't know, Madison!"

He smiled. "I think you're about to tell me."

When Patrice fixed her eyes on the grass blurring outside her window, Madison switched off the radio, though it wasn't loud. "Go on."

"Saying it makes me sound pretty unsophisticated, especially in this vastly enlightened age. I feel like an idiot."

She pushed back a strand of escaping hair and repinned it into her topknot. Madison watched the slender, lifting arms, the breasts outlined beneath her soft, print blouse. She realized the object of his rousing stare and swiftly lowered her arms and worried over a fingernail.

"I'm not on the pill, Madison."

For a moment he contemplated his driving, thinking how difficult it had been for her to confess such a thing to him. "Patri—"

"I'm sorry."

She breathed a long, unwieldly sigh, and Madison swerved off the highway and onto the paved expanse of a service station. He didn't draw up to the self-service island but left the engine running. He would have gathered her into his arms, but he didn't think she would allow anyone to touch her at this moment. He watched her studying her bare toes peeping from her sandals.

"Does that worry you?"

"Of course. Doesn't it worry you?"

He laughed. "No, it doesn't worry me a whit."

Her shoulders lifted. "Well, perhaps everything will be all right. I mean, just one time might not do it. And it won't ever happen again."

Meaning to recapture the straying lock of hair that refused to stay pinned, Madison recklessly leaned toward her. Patrice leaned backward, her eyes raking over his contented face, puzzled.

"I hope you are." He shrugged. "Pregnant, I mean. Then you'll have to marry me."

She felt her eyes widen with incredulity. "You really mean that, don't you?"

"Yes."

"Well." She pinched the bridge of her nose, hardly able to believe his calmness. "I wouldn't *have* to marry you."

He coughed discreetly. "But you would."

She frowned. "Anyway, I'm sure I'm not. I don't know what got into me last night. I just . . . lost control for a minute. Or something. And don't get the idea just because it happened once . . ." She sighed dismally.

Madison steered the pickup beside a gas pump. His sympathy for her was much more than he allowed to show. "It's okay." He smiled at her, turned off the engine, and reached for the door handle. "Honest. I understand."

No you don't, she thought. He didn't understand anything. How could he know he was the first man she'd ever wanted to touch her forever, to never stop? How could he guess that she had remembered they weren't taking precautions, but she was too drugged to do anything except drown in the liquid heat of his desire? No, he didn't understand at all.

While Madison pumped gas, Patrice walked to the soft-drink machine and discovered she had no quarters. Ambling back, seeing that one of the mechanics from the service station had wandered over to chat with Madison about the engine of the truck, she positioned herself behind Madison's right shoulder.

He glanced up from pointing to the carburetor he had installed and smiled.

In a meek, wifely manner, Patrice smiled back. "Could I have some quarters, please?"

The mechanic, wiping his hands, said, "There's a dollar-bill changer inside, ma'am."

Patrice felt as if the man assumed they were married. Madison coolly drew out a handful of change and offered it to her. Flushing slightly, she picked over his pennies and nickels and dimes to ferret out two quarters.

Thoroughly enjoying her nearness and her touch, Madison moistened his lips as she met his smirk. She jingled the coins in the palm of her hand and narrowed her eyes. Her look said, *Wipe that arrogance off your face, Mr. Brannen.*

He had the last word, however, for he called after her.

"Wait a minute, honey." As she paused he took two steps toward her and fished out his wallet to remove a credit card. "Pay for the gas while you're in there."

What a chess player he was! If she refused to sign her name on the receipt, the mechanic would assume they were lovers. If she did, they would look very, very married.

Disregarding the perfectly vile devilment in his eyes, Patrice snatched the credit card from his fingers. "Whatever you want"—she made a face—"*honey.*"

She sauntered into the office with a willowy swing of her hips. She hoped she set his teeth grinding. When she returned, she thrust the receipt into his hand and refused to look at him.

"Thank you," he said, mockery in his expression.

"Perhaps you'd like me to start doing your grocery shopping and pay your other bills," she snapped and pivoted around to murmur privately, "I can do windows and fold laundry, too."

Her bristling independence intrigued him. He motioned her up into the cab and climbed in himself.

"My, my, how like a little wife we've become, Patrice," he said as they put distance between them and the service station. "Complete with nagging and asking for money."

"You could do worse."

Again he laughed, then clapped a hand on her knee, which was crossed over the other. She pushed the hand away, but he only grabbed her wrist and pulled her toward him.

"I can't talk to you way over there," he teased.

"Nothing is ever perfect, Madison." Her pique simmered for several minutes. "Don't you think it's about time you told me about this land we're going to see?"

Madison's shrug had a distinct air of guilt. "Actually," he hedged, "it's a little more involved than just a piece of land. Though it is that!" After a hesitation, he added, "I'm taking you to see Miles and my mother."

At first Patrice didn't speak. Madison felt her digesting the implications of meeting his mother. He feared she would feel he was pressing her, which he was actually doing. But last night had cleared up any doubts he might have had. He intended to go all the way with this woman: the engagement ring, the wedding, the honeymoon, the babies.

"I might have known you'd do this," she said finally, pouting a fascinating lower lip.

"They have to meet you sometime."

"Really? Whose rule book did you find that in?"

He prudently straightened his face and kept his eyes glued to the highway. "I make my own rules. If I'd told you beforehand, you wouldn't have come and you know it."

"I know what you're thinking."

Madison quirked one protesting brow, since he was

remembering the smooth flatness of her stomach, how wonderfully smooth her legs were, and that inner part of her thighs, which was the softest place on earth.

She trudged on. "You think you'll ply me with all the domestic assets you have—your mother, your land, Miles. But it won't work, Madison. I told you before. I can't take a chance as serious as marriage. Not with my track record."

"Oh, damn," he muttered. "I guess you think everything would be fine if we just lived together for a while, sort of a trial run."

Patrice inclined her head at him, surprised that he would bring it up. "I would be more open to that than I would be to the subject of marriage."

He threw an aggravated glare outside at nothing, then at her. "Thanks, but no thanks. I tried it once. It's not for me."

The chill that swept through the cab of the pickup would have turned water to ice.

Patrice sat offended and tall. "Oh? Really, then I—"

"You what?"

"Nothing."

"You were going to say something."

"No, I wasn't!" she cried, then forced her voice ludicrously calm. She could have been talking to herself. "It's nothing to me. It's your life. What you do with it is immaterial to me. See whom you please. Live with whomever you please."

"Why you're jealous," he said, low enough that she could have missed hearing it.

But Patrice didn't miss hearing it. She would have heard it if he had only thought it. Swiveling on the seat, unaware that her skirt was pulling aside to give him a marvelous view of leg and thigh, even the seductive trim of her panties, she leaned forward.

"I—am—not—jealous!" Her color rose. "I've never been jealous, not even of my sister, and certainly not of a man's lover."

"And you're the prettiest little liar. You really have got great legs, Patrice."

Her heaved sigh could have been an obscenity, it was so full of overtones. "You're not going to tell me about it, are you?"

"No."

She snatched down the traitorous skirt and crossed her legs, pressing her knees together with excessive modesty.

Madison smothered his mirth. "You should give yourself that last-minute once-over," he advised. "We'll be there in about five minutes."

Patrice's once-over was a miffed inspection into her compact to find glittering green eyes and a face glowing with the luscious tint of recent love. She hadn't shampooed her hair, but it gleamed in its topknot. She hadn't particularly planned her skirt and blouse, either; but her sandals, which were from a beautiful Italian store, made up for a multitude of other transgressions. She repaired her lipstick and snapped the compact shut.

For a moment she studied his implacable profile. "What was her name?" she asked out of the blue.

Madison didn't look at her. "Whose name?" he drawled with infuriating innocence.

Her teeth gritted with irritation. "What you are is unrepeatable."

He laughed.

Before she could think of anything cuttingly brilliant enough to retort, he turned off the main road and whipped onto a gravel one. A cyclone of dust spun out behind them. A small country store with COCA-COLA lettered across its roof lay on their left. A half-dozen pickups were parked haphazardly about the rural oasis. Gunnysacks of potatoes were stacked about the outside wall with the soft-drink crates. A delivery truck from the city had just unloaded its freight and was backing around to leave.

The driveway leading to the modest frame house was rather short. The yard, Patrice thought, was the house's best asset. Great trees threw most of the lawn into comfortable, inviting shadows. The house wasn't large, but was the kind she liked instantly with its clothesline in the back with snowy sheets billowing in the breeze, and fruit trees behind the garage, well kept and flourishing. A garden plot, visible from the front, was crowded with beans and corn and staked tomatoes. A prolific array of flowerbeds bordered the garden, as well as the scrupulous little house.

"It's marvelous," she said, loving it. "Were you raised here?"

"I spent my teens here. Then Dad died, and I went off to college, then to Nam. I haven't spent nearly the time here lately that I would like to. My land is to the south; forty-seven acres."

Before they could alight from the pickup, the front screen door swept open and slammed with a clatter. A young boy, all arms and legs in cutoff jeans and a white T-shirt, raced across the yard followed by a barking bundle of yipping, buff-colored spaniel.

"Madison!" he shrieked and wrapped everything about the tall man as Madison swept him up in his arms.

For a moment the stream of excited boyish chatter, mingled with the spaniel's curious sniffing, absorbed all of Patrice's attention. Presently, from over his uncle's shoulder, Miles gazed down at her with eyes so brown, so startlingly older than his years, she had difficulty in looking away. She smiled. The ghost of a smile flitted across his lips.

A movement from the porch caught her attention. Patrice watched apprehensively as Virginia Brannen stepped out into the sunlight that glanced off the steps.

The woman had lost the slenderness of youth, but she wasn't heavy. She was a big-boned woman, almost as tall as her son. From where Patrice stood, she could read a number of things about Virginia from the way she wiped her hands on her apron in a manner that said, *I've lived longer than I want to*. And the knotted veins in her legs that said, *I was never a girl*. Her braids looped over her head in a completely unfashionable coiffure. Patrice liked her immediately.

The woman smiled at her grandson's tenacity; Madison had difficulty in prying him loose. As Madison stepped toward his mother Miles tagged closely on his heels.

"Hello, Mom." He kissed her cheek. "I brought someone with me."

"I see you have. Are you going to invite her in or shall I?"

Madison swung his arm out in an inviting arc, and Patrice obediently stepped beside him. She smiled and said the correct things, and all the time she wondered if Madison had brought other women to this farm. No man could live past thirty and not be seriously involved at some time in his life! What was she getting into?

As she preceded them up the steps Virginia Brannen sized up Patrice with the skill of a lifetime. She accurately figured Patrice to be a strong woman, of fine character, a woman who had taken her licks from life. She supposed the latter because of a lurking hunger deep in her eyes, something she guessed Patrice didn't know existed. She had seen the same quiet desperation in Madison's eyes when he had returned from Vietnam. And Rose's, too, back in the years when her daughter's face was still soft.

"Rosie's coming today," Miles announced without a flicker of change in his expression, one way or another.

For an infinitesimal moment Madison received and telegraphed a message of concern back to his mother. Although Patrice observed it, she didn't understand it.

"Well," he said briskly, "that's lucky for both of us,

127

isn't it, cowboy?" He met his mother's eyes again as he asked Miles, "Your mother comes down a lot these days, does she?"

Miles, with six-year-old exuberance, happily supplied the information. "She sent me a birthday present, Madison. Some new jeans and a shirt. You wanna see?"

The lines about Madison's mouth tensed, and Patrice grew uneasy. For Miles to call his mother by her Christian name was a bright flag of trouble. Madison obviously loved the boy very much. Pretending to be happy when Rose hadn't come for his nephew's birthday cost him a great deal. The pain in this very house was so strong it was physically palpable.

"Sure, run and get 'em." Madison playfully ruffled the boy's hair. "While you're gone we'll get a glass of Mom's famous iced tea."

Virginia slowly leveled her glance with her son's. "I didn't make iced tea. I made lemonade."

"Then we'll have a glass of your famous lemonade, young lady. Come on, Patrice. Don't mind Mom. She's of the old school. Her words are few and her heart is large. How's the washing machine, Mom?"

Virginia got down four glasses. The decor of the room was an exact equivalent of her personality—without frills or splendor, utilitarian, functional, immensely comforting.

"Have a seat, Miss Harrows," Virginia invited.

Patrice almost corrected her, telling her that she wasn't a "Miss" Harrows, but Madison caught her look and smiled. Would Virginia disapprove of her if she knew she had been married before? Keeping prudently silent, she thanked her for the lemonade and sipped.

"Whatever you said was wrong with the machine, Madison," Virginia reported straightaway, "wasn't the trouble. It still won't spin."

Madison's frown was a combination of loving indulgence and irritation at himself. "I have two degrees in engineering and I can't fix one damn washing machine. What have you been doing, Mom, beating the clothes on a rock?"

Virginia was obviously used to Madison's badgering. She pursed her mouth at her son. "Don't swear in this house, and I'm not exactly helpless, Madison. I wash out what few things Miles and I need by hand. I've never been overly fond of machines and you know it."

Twisting his mouth into a grotesque threat, Madison made the motion of breaking her neck. "How many times do I have to tell you, Mom? This is the twentieth century. There's no need for you working so hard. Now I'm going to have a new washing machine sent out here, and if you don't use it, do you know what I'll do?"

Virginia braced one careworn hand over another. "I'm the mother and you're the son. I have first say. I'll not have you spending your hard-earned money on me. If I feel that I need a machine, I'll buy one. Not until."

Muttering under his breath that he had never seen such a stubborn woman in all his life, Madison sipped his lemonade and dryly observed to Patrice, "I hope you're in no hurry to get home. I'll have to take another look at that monster. She's so stubborn she'd refuse to accept one if I had it sent out. You don't mind, do you?"

A smile teased Patrice's mouth. "I don't blame her, Madison."

From across the kitchen Virginia Brannen stilled, listening, though she didn't comment.

Madison mumbled something about, "Oh, you do, do you?"

"We women are always at the mercy of a machine," Patrice explained. "If the car breaks down, we can't fix it. If the washer goes, the chances are we're helpless. After a while it begins to be a contest. Sometimes it's much easier to do it the old way, with muscle. That way they don't win entirely."

Virginia allowed a half smile. In that flicker of humor Patrice thought she read more compassion, more unspoken understanding, than she had ever seen in her own mother's face.

"Sometimes it nearly kills you," Virginia agreed. "I know it costs more money in the long run. Maybe years off my life. But at least they don't win."

Patrice nodded and smiled her pleasure over the top of the glass. "It's the principle of it, Madison. The pride."

Madison said he didn't understand and couldn't disagree more. Virginia informed him that she wouldn't expect a spoiled young man to understand a thing like that. The repartee was so playful, so warm, that Patrice found it more tender than a lot of showy hugging and kissing.

Madison slammed his open palm down on the table with a rousing clap.

"Both of you should be declared dangerous to your own selves," he growled. "Well, Miles, let's have a look at that shirt. Enough of this woman's pointless fussing."

Miles excuted a slow turn in the center of the kitchen, proudly displaying a nice western shirt. "It would look better if I had some boots, huh?"

Madison clapped his knee and the boy climbed on. "It's fine, just like it is. What d'you want an old pair of boots for?"

"So I can be a real cowboy, pardner."

"Come on then, let's show Patrice the farm if you're such a cowboy."

As the three of them neared the banks of a respectable-sized lake, Miles dashed ahead, calling back to them, his feet dancing with anticipation.

"Skip a rock, Madison!" he crowed. "Clear across. Like you used to do!"

Around them, on all sides, rolled gentle, sloping acres belonging to Madison and his mother. Prime land, enclosed with well-tended fences and thickets whose undergrowth had been meticulously cleared away. Fallen trees had been dragged out and cut for firewood, and the land was so thickly seeded it was green, even in late summer.

Madison squinted out over the glistening mirror of water and began unbuttoning his shirt. Pulling it free of his trousers, he let the tails flap tantalizingly about his hips.

"Maybe I forgot how," he remarked idly.

"Not you."

Letting them bicker in their man-boy way, Patrice drew back into the cool shadows of a tree and leaned against its inviting trunk. This man had made love to her, she mused. He had held her closely in those arms, had crushed her with that weight, and placed her hand upon his hip and whispered, "Touch me." Now he was so comfortable, so easy with her, that he absorbed himself with other things, knowing she was there, that their silences were as good as their talk. Until he turned presently and called to her, his hips braced on the backs of his heels as he knelt, she thought he had forgotten about her.

"Patrice, where'd you go?"

"I'm here," she called back, stepping from the shadows. She moved to where Miles bent over the stones Madison was selecting. The youngster was rapt, his hands braced on his knees.

"What d'you think?"

Patrice laughed. "I think you two are a couple of crazy M & Ms."

Miles giggled at her reference to their initials.

Madison threw her a knowing glance. "Candy-coated and everything?" he drawled.

Patrice blushed to the roots of her hair, knowing what he meant. "Some would call it that," she admitted.

Holding his palm outstretched, filled with carefully

selected stones, smooth and flat, he asked softly, "What do *you* call it?"

Clasping her hands behind her back, she gazed fondly down at the two of them. "The antics of a mad lady."

Laughing, Madison rose and, at the same time, flexed his body gracefully. He sent a stone skimming over the placid surface of the lake, leaving a trail of bursting stars in its wake.

As Miles eagerly made a less skillful attempt Madison turned to peer down at her. The color of his eyes darkened as they locked with hers, holding her, caressing as tenderly as his hands had loved her the night before.

"I call it nice," he said gently and brushed a knuckle across her cheek. "I call it very, very nice."

Chapter Seven

The afternoon glided past on lazy, butterfly wings, and Patrice lost track of time as she watched Madison romp with his nephew through a large unmowed expanse of grassland. The sky was a radiant blue, filled with just enough clouds to offer patches of welcome shade, but not enough to ward off a ravenous thirst.

Life was backward, she mused as the play neared its end. Though there were many people in the world who didn't want their children, had never wanted them, Madison was not one of them. He should be surrounded by children. He was a natural father. It wasn't really fair.

"Do you like it?" Madison asked as they strolled lackadaisically back to the house.

Miles was tiring, and he trudged beside them, a pole balanced upon his shoulder like a foraging pioneer. Taking advantage of the lull, Madison reached for Patrice and drew her so near beside him that their sides touched as they walked. One hand curled low upon her hip and she didn't protest. The caress felt right—settled, peaceful. Both of them watched their steps stirring tiny poffs of dust in the old, little-used roadbed.

"I love it," she said. "I've lived in town all my life. Don't you plan to come back to it?"

Madison gazed out over his land as if he had considered it long and often. "Someday, when everything is right."

"When you can retire?"

He grinned down at her. "When I'm a doddering old man? Not on your life. Country is for kids and dogs and horses and picnics and all those good things."

She read his thoughts. She knew his dream. It was a perfect dream for him, and she knew he was trying to place her in that dream.

"Madison, you—"

"Just let me have my fantasies," he cut her off.

Her breath caught, and Madison missed a step. When his balance shifted, even this small amount, Patrice's concern darted immediately to his knees. Her hand tightened on his arm. But Madison's interests, after tossing a glance at Miles's oblivion, was not for his legs. If they had been alone he would have kissed her. For one brief second she feared he might do it anyway. She stiffened.

But his shoulders only lowered, and he smiled sheepishly at himself, then chuckled. "I'm going to build a house someday," he told her. "Back by the lake. I'll put a road"—he gestured—"through . . . there."

Madison pointed as he talked, and Miles, having heard it all before, poked about in the grass with his pole and disturbed fat grasshoppers until they buzzed madly in retreat.

Patrice followed Madison's outflung hand and caught a swift breath when he crooked his arm about her neck. His fingers inched over the swell of her breast, and he turned himself in toward her. They stood quite close, and Patrice wriggled against such boldness.

"Madison!" she whispered. "Be careful, for heaven's sake!"

"Miles needs to see two people who love each other. He hasn't known much love between a man and a woman, God knows. And how can I be careful? You're driving me mad, woman."

Nervously disengaging herself, she unsteadily shoved her hands into the pockets of her skirt. "Well, at least *I* haven't been running around all afternoon with my shirt half off."

Madison glanced down at his tanned expanse of chest and belly. "The macho in me, I guess." He grimaced comically.

Grasping a tiny curl of black hair as it disappeared beneath his belt, Patrice tweaked it quite hard. She meant for it to hurt.

He yelped.

"You should wear a medal inscribed with 'I love me,'" she taunted. "We'd better get back to the house, Madison, before you make me lose control of myself."

"Witch." He laughed and began buttoning his shirt. "A twenty-seven-year-old witch."

Patrice threw him a withering glare. "Twenty-*five*."

Trudging several steps beyond him, pretending a fit of pique, she fell into step with Miles. His head turned slightly in acknowledgment, but he said nothing.

"Have you ever considered building a raft for the lake, Miles?" she asked. She was amazed at the swift interest he showed. She had obviously said the magic words.

"Do you know how to build stuff?" His eyes were a piercing brown, not easily deceived.

She giggled. "I guess I do. When I was in high school I took wood shop with the boys. It upset everything terribly and made the school break their rule. But I learned how to build stuff, yes."

Miles peered up at her with new respect. So did Madison as he ambled up beside them.

"Could you build a raft?" the boy persisted. "It would have to really float, you know."

Laughing, Patrice caught the boy's hand and swung it between them. Much to her surprise he didn't withdraw it. He only grew thoughtful. Beside them, with an expression of love she was unaware of, Madison smiled at them.

Miles grew generous with his enthusiasm. "I could draw you a picture," he volunteered excitedly. "What about a sail? Do you think it should have a sail?"

For a moment she considered. "It depends on how deep the lake is. A long pole might do well, like the big ferry boats used to use."

"I could do that," he boasted importantly.

As Patrice bent her head, having innocently won the boy's confidence with her genuine friendship, Madison wondered at his good fortune in ever finding her. Convincing her to marry him wouldn't be easy, he predicted, but the best things in life never were. He loved her very much.

Miles fell into silence, and he presently tipped his head up at her. "Miss Harrows?"

Patrice flicked a sprig of hair from his eyes. "What, sir?"

"Are you the lady that ran over Madison's Kawasaki?"

What could she do but laughingly grit her teeth at the tall man beside her? Turning suddenly, she came down on his shoulder with a doubled fist, then skittered out of his reach.

"That's low, Madison!" she railed at him. "Really low!"

Madison dodged her pelting too late, then darted after her. The chase was over before it had hardly begun. Madison captured her with an arm about her waist and, despite her blustering counterattack, restrained her flailing arms.

"Hang on there!" he yelled. "Now cut that out. I never said a thing that wasn't true."

"I offered to pay for that!" she sputtered, feigning a spectacular pout. "At least give me the benefit of that!" She jerked herself from his much too-willing imprisonment. "So like a man."

Madison, giving in to an impulse that had tempted him all morning, impudently planted his hand upon her bottom with a resounding smack. She yelped, much to Miles's amusement.

Seeing the youngster's delight at watching two adults play, Patrice grabbed his thin arm and looped it through hers. "Miles will protect me." She sniffed haughtily.

"He'd better be good," puffed Madison as he caught up with them, "because you're on my list."

Coyly cutting her eyes, Patrice tossed her head. She knew he loved for her to flirt. "At the top?"

He pretended to consider. "Within the top three, at least."

She scowled at him. "I'm going to have to do something about your attitude."

He chuckled and bent his head near her ear. "I wouldn't dare stop you," he murmured. "I'm real easy, love."

Fearing Miles would grasp too much of Madison's erotic implications, she moved beyond him. "You're crazy is what you are."

Miles, however, lengthened his stride to that of his beloved uncle. He watched their shadows jerk and reshape themselves along the uneven ground. He thought their banter was the most wonderful thing he had ever heard. That they included him in it made him feel truly important, like a man. He wished he belonged to them. Why couldn't they have been his mother and father?

* * *

Upon returning to the farmhouse, Madison scrounged up a handful of tools, a screwdriver, a couple of wrenches, a hammer, and ordered her to follow him to the laundry room. Patrice asked him if he were going to beat the washer into submission.

"Don't get those clothes dirty," Virginia called after him. "I don't want you getting messed up because of that old washer."

"Sometimes I think that woman will be the death of me," Madison mumbled fondly under his breath.

Motioning Patrice with him into a room off the back porch, he swung open the door to an old-fashioned washhouse. The modest addition had no window, only a door, which cast a large shaft of sunshine across a cement floor. One lone shelf displayed Virginia's simple washing items and a various array of paint cans. In one corner leaned a hoe, one rake, and two shovels. Despite the fresh summer breeze, the air smelled musty and damp.

"This was my clubhouse when I was fourteen," Madison reminisced. "The neighbor boy and I slept out here several times. Set the place afire once."

Patrice laughed at him. "Madison, is there anything you haven't done?"

He leveled a thoughtful look at her, nodding. "Several. A number of those have to do with you."

Sobering, Patrice hurriedly moved to the washing machine. She smoothed its lines absently. As long as they were scrapping she felt safe. When Madison grew earnest, as he just had, some strange greediness gnawed at her. She wanted to be closer to him than anyone else, to do things with him that no one else did, and she was unused to being selfish with a man's affections.

Madison dumped his tools beside him on the floor with a clatter.

"Well, you might as well put yourself to some good

use," he said. "If I tip this thing over so I can get underneath with the flashlight, can you balance it? No weight or anything. Just keep it from falling on me?"

The expression on her face was transformed into a delightful menace. "Now I know why your mother argues with you all the time, you chauvinist. Of course I can hold the dumb thing up. Go on."

Madison, not nearly as confident of her prowess as she, arranged the machine where it teetered on its two back legs. Then he proceeded to poke the upper half of his body beneath it. He examined first one thing, then another, grumbling and talking to himself all the while. When he inadvertently tugged on the culprit connection, he triggered a short. The bare light bulb dangling from the ceiling went black and cast the corners of the shed into thick shadows.

"Damn!"

The popping of the fuse startled Patrice. As she flinched and as Madison attempted to lift his head, she nearly dropped her end of the machine. It jostled her back against the wall and pressed, with unrelenting weight, into her waist. It felt as if it would cut her in two.

"Madison," she choked. "I—can't—hold—this. . . ."

"Just a minute."

He was up in a flash, jerking the machine around to free her from the projection of crushing metal. It scraped rawly against the cement as he swung it about, and Patrice found the weight of the washing machine swiftly replaced with a very virile, very male weight. Madison's face bent only a few, unsteady inches above her own.

"Are you okay?"

They were both breathing hard, and she didn't think it was caused by the agitation generated by a blown fuse.

"Thank you," she said and vaguely attempted to step around him. "I'm fine."

"You're welcome, but I haven't done anything. Yet."

She could feel the power of his ribs against hers, the muscles of his waist deliberately straining, pressing her back until there was nowhere to go.

"I can't get by," she protested feebly, knowing full well he was about to kiss her. Then she said the first thing that jumped into her head. "I hope you didn't blow every fuse in the house."

He blew into her eyelashes and made her blink. "Only mine, darling. Kiss me."

"What if someone comes?" she squeaked. It was all flooding back upon her, the marvel of what they had done the night before. He wasn't a stranger to her now; she wasn't so innocent now, and it both pleasured her and embarrassed her.

"I don't care if the world comes. Stop talking."

His mouth was touching hers, nibbling, his tongue flicking against her teeth, his hands busy between them, searching for the bottom of her blouse and pulling it free. His palms slid up her back, cool on her blistering skin. When his fingers began toying with the edge of her bra, invading beneath it, moving in front to manipulate the tiny clip, she wrested her lips from his.

"No," she said against his jaw, feeling her innocence escaping even further away. "I mean it. You should finish fixing the washer."

"Damn the washer. Put your arms around my neck." His kiss wandered to the nape of her own silky neck.

"It's wrong to do this here."

"It's never wrong to do this."

"What if—"

"Quiet, Patrice." His kisses traced a path across her jaw. Fighting his hands seemed hopeless. One fit gently about her chin, refusing to let her lower her head, and the other reached low to skim beneath the hem of her skirt. She felt her skirt lifting scandalously high, bunching about her waist as he fit his palm over the curve of her hip.

Now she struggled in earnest. *"What are you doing?"*

Madison leaned from her with the upper part of his body. His smile, though pleasant, frayed around the edges, and the muscles in his neck darkened warmly. "I'm trying to seduce you, love. Aren't you ever going to stop haggling and kiss me?"

Even as he said the words he ground himself against her. Patrice thought it was the most dangerous predicament she had ever been trapped in. But her head was tipping back, and his lips were parting hers, opening them, tasting them with delicious inquiry.

"I'm not haggling," she mumbled into his mouth. Then she was silenced as he fastened his lips to hers and moved against her with a strengthening rhythm.

He was deadly! His taste and his smell were treacherous! She felt herself becoming ridiculously giddy and tingling, incapable of reasoning. Slowly, as if she were two people—one alert, one helpless—she melted into the angular strength of his body.

The precariousness of where they were didn't bother Madison. Crushing her hard to him, he began trifling with the lace of her panties. To Patrice, he was suddenly transformed into a miracle of trespassing fingers and bold, possessive liberties. She felt herself burning, horrified at the way she turned to liquid. And when she struggled to remind him of where they were, she only made it easier for him. One hand slipped beneath the lace to discover a response she was incapable of feigning, fingers moving upward, finding, tempting, scattering her senses like so much folly.

"Are you mad?" she whimpered into the kiss he was already retrieving.

"Insane. How do you do this to me?"

Virginia's discreet call from the back door of the house was the only thing that saved her. Patrice was grateful for it; she wasn't certain she could have withstood the blinding urgency Madison had unleashed inside her.

She slumped against him. "Oh," she said, exhausted.

Madison suffered a matching difficulty in gathering his own scattered senses. "A man's work is never done," he muttered bleakly and readjusted his trousers.

"Shh!" she choked and awkwardly began to repair herself. "Answer your mother, you scoundrel."

"Miss Harrows." Virginia stood in the center of her own kitchen, troubled as she introduced everyone. "This is my daughter, Rose, and her friend . . ."

"Bert," Rose quickly supplied. "Bert Stevenson. He's in sales."

The strained tensions that peppered over the room were as many and as varied as the people in it. But reactions, especially covert ones, were Patrice's strong point. Madison's younger sister, surprisingly pretty, monopolized the room though she was doing nothing. The tall, thin man hovering behind her blended into the background as a way of protecting himself. Virginia's uneasiness was a simple one. Her arms folded across her bosom in a hugging mannerism that was impossible to misinterpret; she feared an unhappy scene.

The only point that truly concerned Patrice, since Madison could cope with his own hostility to Rose, was Miles's shrinking uncertainty. As the adults stumbled through their awkward pretensions, Miles gawked at the strange man behind his mother with dread and wonder.

"Well, Mama," Rose chattered with a counterfeit enthusiasm that didn't relieve any of the strain. "It certainly is hot in the country. You need an air conditioner out here."

To have something to do, Virginia stiffly offered Bert a glass of lemonade and refilled everyone else's glass. She invited them to find somewhere to sit.

Patrice preferred to stand near the door behind Miles as people found chairs. Rose stepped toward her son, then stooped to the floor, her expensive skirt sweeping it like a queen's train.

She motioned to him with her fingers. "Come here, darlin'," she cooed. "Give your mama a hug."

Bert attempted small talk with Madison as Miles dutifully wound his small arms about his mother's neck. Madison ignored the man.

Miles repeated his welcome speech to his mother in a shrill, quivering voice. "It's nice you came to see us, Rosie."

Once Miles had performed what was expected of him, he timidly withdrew to stand beside the more familiar skirt of his grandmother. Virginia didn't offer any demonstrations, not a ruffling of his hair nor a pat to his shoulder. She simply stood there like a bulwark.

Though it was unwitting, free of malice, Miles's detachment did not go unnoted by Rose. She wasn't an insensitive woman, and her spurned maternity, especially before the man she had brought home with her, was a glaring transgression. She felt enormous pressure to save face.

Rose threw a look of smiling reproach at her mother. She laughed at her son. "Why, I'm your mama, sugar pie. You shouldn't be calling me Rosie. Don't you think you've about outgrown that? Why don't we just make it 'Mother' from now on? Okay, sweetie?"

A sound of disagreement growled deep in Madison's chest, but Virginia's puckered brows warned him to stay out of it. Wishing she weren't a witness to this, Patrice shifted her weight uncomfortably.

Rose grasped Miles's hand and tried to pull him toward her, to insist on his acceptance of her maternal petting. Miles, however, was too frightened to think clearly. He dug in his heels and strained backward, bending like a bow in the opposite direction.

His reluctance embarrassed Rose. "I have someone I want you to meet, Miles."

The jerk she gave Miles was slight, but in such a tense setting it could have been a cuff on the jaw. Those watching began shifting restlessly. They sipped their drinks and focused their eyes on anything except at the stricken boy.

"Come on now." Rosie pushed Miles forward. "Shake Bert's hand like a proper little gentleman."

Bert, angular-featured, dressed in skimpy knit pants and a plaid shirt, looked as if he wished he were on the moon or in Siberia, anywhere except in this room. He glanced first at Virginia—half in apology for adding to the discomfort of the child, half for being in the room at all—then to Madison. Trouble from the frowning, dark-haired man was the last thing he wanted.

"Rose, honey . . ." he muttered.

Rose interrupted Bert's protest. "It's all right, darlin'. Miles can at least shake your hand. He mustn't be so rude." Her voice became gritty. "Come here, Miles."

With his fingers twisting into her skirt, Miles looked up at his grandmother, misty eyes pleading. "Mamaw?" he choked.

Virginia mutely nodded to her grandson. She stoically urged him to do what must be done, instilling him with her own strength of will to do it.

Looking very small, very deserted, Miles proved the influence of his grandmother's love. He set his quivering jaw, squared his thin shoulders, and forced himself to step toward Bert, hand outstretched.

A hard knot swelled in Patrice's throat at this small display of bravery. It wasn't anything monumental, but for Miles it was a grave test of manhood. Though she was a stranger here, she found herself wanting to step forward, to declare that enough was enough.

With a surprising amount of understanding, Bert bent on one knee. "Hello, Miles," he said gently.

"Kinda tough on a guy with so many grown-up faces everywhere, ain't it?"

Nodding dumbly, Miles let the man pump his hand a couple of times. Rose stood triumphantly beside Bert's knee, looking down on the drama. When Miles threw a pleading glance at Madison, the maternal smile wavered but did not disappear entirely.

The second the ritual was done, Miles snatched his hand free and spun on his heel. Forgetting his pretense of adulthood, he raced for Madison and threw himself so violently against his legs, the glowering man stumbled backward.

Over the head of the boy Madison sent Rose a look that would have made a weaker woman dash from the room in tears. Rose, however, lifted her pretty head and only broadened her smile. She was hurting badly.

"Well, Madison, dear," she purred, "I see you haven't been letting moss grow under your feet, have you?"

Madison glanced at the wall beside him, the mannerism of a man strained to the limit. Miles, having no idea that he had just chosen his uncle over his mother, followed the path of the grim gesture. He realized he was the center of something intensely disagreeable. Inching backward, he pressed tightly against Patrice's leg.

The muscle in Madison's jaw leaped to life, knotting repeatedly. "If you mean what I think you mean, Rose, I'd take my own advice if I were you. It's not your feet I worry about."

The remark was too subtle for Miles to understand, but everyone else knew that he was accusing his sister of immorality. It was a terrible thing to say in private, much less in this room.

Virginia's head dropped in abject misery, and Bert looked as if he could crawl through the floor. The glares they threw at each other were as cold as steel, demanding a resolution.

Madison took one outraged step toward his sister, fists clenched. Patrice almost jerked back when she felt the small boyish hand clutch hers. In the antagonism, everyone seemed to have forgotten the wide, perceptive eyes that took everything into an impressionable brain.

Tipping upward, Miles looked at Patrice with brimming brown eyes. Tears spilled and slid slowly down his cheeks.

"What did I do wrong?" he said in a strangled voice. His knotted fists ground into his streaming eyes. "I'm sorry!" he wailed.

The heartbroken sob broke the tension in the room. Virginia's grieved spirit flashed to that of Patrice. Never in her life had Patrice had an older woman look to her for anything, especially help. But Virginia was begging her silently: *He's reaching out to you. If you can do anything to help, please do it.*

With a look at Madison that told him he should have known better, Patrice clasped Miles's hand firmly.

"If you will all excuse us," she said in a clear high voice, "Miles and I have been discussing plans to build a raft. Miles, if you have a sheet of paper and a pencil, why don't we get started while your mother and Madison have a chance to talk?"

She didn't wait to see if she had done the right thing or not. She acted purely on instinct, but knew that Virginia was grateful to her. Madison probably was too. Rose would undoubtedly despise her, thinking she was an interfering crazy woman.

No one mattered now but the weeping boy. She drew him from the room, and paper and pencil were promptly forgotten. They walked out the front door without speaking and down the steps. The sunshine blinded them, and they kept on walking, down the dusty road, until soon they could see the little grocery store far in the distance.

"My," she said at last, breaking the silence. "If I had

146

thought, I would've brought my purse and we could have had something to drink."

The round face beamed up at her, streaked from where tears had dried on his cheeks. Patrice impulsively stooped to wipe away the stains.

"I have three quarters," he chirped. "Madison says a man should never be without money in his pocket."

Fearing it was her turn to weep now, Patrice hugged him tightly. "What a marvel you are, Miles. You don't mind buying an older woman a Coke, do you?"

"Mr. Johnson keeps 'em real cold. Some of them have ice in the top."

"That's my favorite way," Patrice agreed, and they hastened their steps and crossed the road.

From Patrice's side of the seat on the way home Madison's moods seemed contradictory. One minute he was thoughtful; he was polite the next; dangerously withdrawn after that. For a time they both escaped into their own thoughts, not risking the ordeal of a conversation. Presently a browned hand fell on her shoulder, startling her.

He drew her into the safe curve of his side. "Isn't it wonderful how nicely a woman fits here?" he said, tired but smiling.

He was grateful for having her now, and she wondered if that fact should frighten her. He had once seen her family in a state of crisis, and now she had seen his. Crises had a strange way of forging people's lives together. And she had promised herself she would remain "emotionally uninvolved" with him!

She leaned her head against his shoulder. "That's not really what you want to say to me, is it?"

Madison sucked at the center of his upper lip. His words, when they came, sounded as if he were thinking them at the precise moment he spoke them.

"I can't let her take Miles away from the farm. I just can't do it. She's trying to prove she's big enough to,

147

that's all. She doesn't want him. She's never wanted him."

"She's his mother."

He went on as if he didn't hear. "I've decided I'm going to ask for custody. At least temporary custody. I'm not sure what that entails, but God, I have to do something."

The alarm bells, which jangled in Patrice's head, made her sit up straight. Tactfully, gently, she withdrew from Madison's embrace. He glanced sideways at her, then back to the highway.

"I have to tell you, Madison, from a professional standpoint I think you don't have a chance. From a friend's standpoint . . . I think it's a mistake."

"Mistake? Why, because I'd be a single parent?"

"That, and the fact that she's his *mother*, Madison."

"She doesn't act like a mother, damn it! She'll take him away and we won't know if he's cold or hungry or sleeping in some blasted car somewhere. No, I won't let that happen."

His dark head shook from side to side with a selfless disagreement she couldn't understand. Who was she to advise? She should stay out of it.

But she didn't follow her own best judgment. "Your mother would be hurt to see the two of you fighting over Miles," she said.

"Mom's already hurt. Miles's best interest is what's at stake here."

Convinced that he was wrong, Patrice listened to her own reasonable argument. "What makes you think you can be a better parent than Rose?" she demanded. "You have your work. No one would be there when Miles needed them, unless you let him continue to live with your mother. There's the housekeeper route, I suppose, but still . . ."

With a glance into the rearview mirror, Madison abruptly veered the pickup off the road. The tires bit into crunching gravel. For another two thousand yards

148

he drove down a country lane cast into the thrusting shadows of evening. The fence on one side was outlined with great trees, beyond which spread a farmer's open clearing.

Leaving the engine running, Madison gripped both of Patrice's shoulders until her head snapped back. His intense hold was so strong he was hurting her, but she guessed he had no idea of this.

The muscle in his jaw clenched before he spoke. "He would have someone if you'd marry me, Patrice."

Her mouth slackened with astonishment as she paled. For numb moments she wondered if he could possibly be so blinded by his trauma that he didn't realize how he was using her. *How could he be so callous?*

She shoved viciously against his chest, but he seemed not to notice. Tearing her gaze away, still twisting from under his biting fingers, she spoke toward the open grassland beyond her.

"You're a very farsighted man, Madison," she said tonelessly.

Her dejection had an effect. Lessening his grip, Madison frowned, then released her. "What d'you mean, farsighted?" he demanded.

It dawned on him then of how it looked. The circumstances of his marriage proposal. He glanced away, then back, his eyes a dark gray. "You don't think I planned this in advance?"

She tried unsuccessfully to keep her lips from trembling. "Yes! Yes, I think you planned it! You needed a wife, you looked for one. And the fact that you threw in the part about loving me, well, that was just your opening argument." Her hands dropped helplessly to her lap. She shook her head. "Oh, Madison."

In the confines of the cab, a temper had its inconveniences. Madison switched off the ignition and slammed the keys to the seat as if they were the cause of all his troubles. Between his teeth he swore a long, blistering oath. He didn't look at her. His hands curved loosely about the steering wheel before his forehead dropped miserably against it.

Before he could soften her with his apologies, Patrice added her final rejection. She instinctively hurt him back.

"How neat you men are, Madison. You work things out in such clever, tidy boxes. And if you need another person to hook it all together, just pick a victim. Any victim. Well, damn it, Madison, I'm tired of being the victim to someone's logic, even your well-motivated one!"

Then he moved across the seat and jerked her around to face him. "You're twisting things, Patrice. You know I would never use you like that. Look at me! I love you. I want to marry you. I'm not wife shopping, not like you mean."

"I don't believe you know *what* you're doing," she mumbled.

His fingers threaded through the hair at the back of her head, and his desperation darkened. "I won't beg you." He ground out the words.

She struck at his hand, but he refused to stop touching her.

"Don't use that tone with me." She gritted out the words.

"Then don't act like a spoiled brat!"

That was the one abuse Patrice could not tolerate from him, the one thing she had been accused of being all her life. Without considering anything except her own outrage, she doubled her fist and swung sideways at his shoulder. The blow glanced off his shoulder harmlessly, but Madison's endurance had ended. His anger erupted as he leaned his body toward hers, his intent drawn in every line of his face. His teeth twinkled dangerously between his lips.

Patrice, fearing him now, for her accusations had not been dealt lightly, flailed her hand for the door handle.

She kicked open the door and jumped lightly to the ground.

"What are you doing?" he lashed out at her. "Come back here."

She walked across the clearing very fast. Her steps crunched crisply into the dead grasses and leaves. They sounded deafening.

Behind her, Madison's door slammed. He followed her with heated strides.

Perhaps she should have stayed in the truck, she thought. He was a strong, volatile man, worried sick about his nephew. She had stung him painfully with her accusations.

Whirling, she threw out a hand to stop him. "Madison?" she pleaded in a small voice.

"Your tongue has a real bite, counselor," he snarled. "And your expertise in distorting the truth is amazing."

"It's *your* insensitivity that's amazing, Madison!"

Patrice knew he had not meant to deliberately wound her. She was aware of his hands shaking when he reached out for her. But that didn't prevent her feminine pride from spurning him.

"Baby-sitters are hired, Mr. Brannen, not married!" she threw at him.

Anger took its natural course like hot lava flowing freely, burning, destroying. Spinning hard, Patrice walked back the way she had come, past the pickup toward the distant traffic of the highway.

In his distress Madison failed to calculate the consequences of what he did. He sprinted after her, catching her, jerking her about until she stumbled against the unyielding wall of his body.

"Don't do this," he rasped. "Don't throw this away."

Though he held her, she wrenched her face away. He gave her a gentle shake.

"Patrice, listen to me. I'm talking about forever. You

can't turn away from what's between us. I won't let you."

She faced him suddenly, her teeth clenched. She struck him, openhanded and hard, with the accusation blazing in her eyes.

"You're no different from Justin."

The wound went deep. He was kissing her before she could breathe, not seeming to care that it wasn't what she wanted. Her nails, burying into the biceps of his arms, cut into the lacing sinews as she wriggled against him. Her legs were tangling with his stronger ones, and her breasts, crushed now to his chest, were no longer an object of pleasure to him.

In desperation to hold on to what he had, Madison plundered his way into the hollows of her mouth. With his bruising lips he set boundaries around her, delivered ultimatums. He treated her as he would an obstacle that deterred him. He forced her.

She told herself he could not hurt her like Justin had. He could not use her as a convenience. Refusing him, then, she made her body inflexible. She held herself away from him in her mind—totally void of response, of feeling, even of anger.

Abruptly Madison released her. The regret that flamed in his eyes was a brilliant blue. Patrice made herself invulnerable to that, too.

Giving him her profile, she said dully, "I want to go home."

"Patrice, love . . ." he began, broken with a remorse that was foreign to anything he had experienced before. "I don't know why I—"

"Please, I want to go home."

No one welcomed the first bite of fall more than Patrice. Not only was she thankful to see the last of the heat, she dreadfully needed a change. Almost any kind would do.

She began the routine of replacing her summer clothes with heavier skirts and blouses, and several of her favorite suits. Seasons changed, she reminded herself, and everyone kept on living. Inside her things had changed, but she, too, must go on. She sat on the floor of her bedroom now, surrounded by shoe boxes and garment bags.

What was Madison doing today? Was he happy? Had he been successful in his petition for custody of Miles? Oh, Lord, would she ever see him again?

Burying her face in her hands, she cursed herself. This was the very thing she had promised herself weeks ago she would not do. It had taken days of excruciating willpower to keep from going to his house and knocking on the door, or from walking to the telephone and swallowing her pride. And that was what it all boiled down to: pride.

Damn! She wasn't going to sit around in her apartment all afternoon and blow a perfectly good weekend. She had a life to get on with. And she would get on with it. She would buy herself a new pair of stockings or treat herself to a salad at Bergdorf's.

Grabbing up a light sweater and a scarf, she swept down the hall, out the elevator and slammed the door to the Ferrari. The engine roared, and she tied the scarf about her head.

She would enjoy eating alone, she told herself. She would have a salad. She would not be lonely for Madison Brannen.

Her waitress, Sally was the name on her pin, was annoyingly inclined to chat. As Patrice dug grooves into her linen napkin Sally went on and on about her divorce as she tossed fresh spinach, mushrooms, Jerusalem artichokes, and bacon. Flourishing her dainty hands cuffed with white ruched frills, she remarked upon Patrice's own long-sleeved shirt, even her new jeans and western boots.

"Oh, I'd like a glass of Chablis, too," Patrice added, giving a sigh of relief as Sally obediently went to fetch it.

"As I live and breathe," a deep masculine voice purred into her left ear.

Patrice jumped, then scooted about in her chair, her face wreathed in a lovely smile. "Paul Nelson. You took a year off my life. What in the world are you doing roaming around loose on a Saturday afternoon?"

Without being invited, the attractive physician dragged up a chair and slouched down on his spine. His eyes devoured her fresh, slender loveliness as if he had never seen her before.

"Have a seat, Paul." She smirked knowingly. "Stop panting."

He had the grace to flush. "Thanks, I will. I've just finished doing what is commonly known as 'the weekend parent' bit. I'm drained, depressed, and seriously considering hanging myself."

The waitress returned with Patrice's wine and quirked her eyebrows at Paul. Then she tilted her chin in surprise at Patrice's skill at hooking a man so quickly.

Paul shook his head, then reconsidered. "Bring me whatever wine she's having," he said.

He leaned forward on his forearms as Patrice hungrily delved into her salad. "You're as beautiful as ever, Patrice. How're you feeling these days? You never come to see me anymore."

Patrice blotted her mouth and ignored the blatant dose of flattery. "I'm fine. The work at Bridgeport's in a constant state of stalemate, but then you know how the conglomerates can tie things up for years. At least they're not acting ugly. My other cases keep me occupied."

Paul toyed with the edge of a neat mustache. He wasn't a startlingly handsome man, but his debonair manners, his image and tastes, were so above average he fit together in a completely pleasant whole.

"And Justin?" he inquired softly.

Finding him unusually obvious, Patrice laid down her fork. "Are you going on a fishing excursion, doctor?"

Laughing, he accepted the wine the waitress placed in front of him. He lifted his glass in a salute. "To intelligent women."

She smiled. "You don't know what you're saying. You're a fan of the docile-female prototype." She lifted her own glass. "To opinionated men."

As he sipped, Paul's smile took on a knowing glint. "I'd like to ask you out, as you have so intelligently figured out. The dilemma I find myself in is wondering if I'd be stepping on anyone's toes or not."

For a fluttering heartbeat of time, Patrice went dark inside. Yes, yes! she wanted to confess to him. There was someone, or *had* been someone. That was changed now. She was desperate to not care. She couldn't care!

She found her hands trembling, and she self-consciously lifted them to her throat. All Paul saw from his side of the table was a delightful hint of coyness.

"What do you have on your mind?" Patrice forced herself to be gay. "My toes are my own, you know. My divorce has been final for months."

Paul's skilled hands, as smooth as any woman's, laced together. He leaned his chin upon them. "Do you play tennis?"

She laughed and executed a restrained backhand with her fork. "Ferociously."

In a movement that was so unexpected, even for him, she guessed, Paul reached across the table and closed one hand over hers. His eyes were richly hazel and clear. "I'm very . . . lonely right now," he told her honestly. "What d'you say to a nice, uncomplicated set at the club?"

What was Madison doing at this very minute? she

wondered crazily. Was he missing her? Was he flirting with some other woman as Paul was flirting with her? Would he even care that she was about to have a date with a man simply to keep from thinking about him? She didn't think so.

She gave herself a mental shaking and flashed her most becoming smile. "I'd like that very much. Only one condition."

"You name it."

"I want to play now."

"Immediately?"

Nodding, she crushed her napkin beside her unfinished salad. "Immediately," she said. Her desperation was so slight that only someone very close to her would have seen it. Paul did not notice.

He grinned and slapped some money on the table. "Be prepared, lady."

Oh, she was that, she told herself as they walked quickly out of the restaurant. Now she was prepared, now that she had nothing to lose anymore.

Chapter Eight

At what point did a person finally stop living by their pride and begin listening to their heart? For weeks Patrice pondered the consequence of this question. She had so many things: a good job, a decent head on her shoulders, a pretty face, a clever tongue. Yet no one knew what was truly inside her. No one except Madison Brannen. And she, in an act of offended propriety had cut him off, severed the ties with the one person who dared to venture into her soul. The last weeks she had buried in work, keeping in touch with her family only through courtesy and praying fiercely each night that all feelings for Madison would vanish with the morning.

For a time she watched the calendar, too. If her worst fears were realized, she would have no choice. She would pick up the telephone and say, "Madison, we have to talk." But time proved that particular calamity was not so.

A month passed before she reached the point where she could neither eat nor sleep for thinking about him.

Her apartment aggravated her. The Ferrari infuriated her. Her job became a worrisome drag. Finally, on a gloomy Friday afternoon, after a perfectly wretched week, she did what she swore she would never, never do.

She let his phone ring a dozen times. When Madison didn't answer, a murky sense of loss seeped through her. Perhaps later. She would try again later, she told herself.

Later, Madison still didn't answer.

At midnight, certain that he would be in bed by now, she dialed again. Nothing.

She sat stone still in the darkness of her bedroom and listened to the quiet. What was he doing that was so important? Was he with a woman? How dare he?

She worried a strand of her hair. A dozen things could be wrong. What if he were ill? What if he had been in a ghastly accident and was in the hospital? She shuddered with a mad impulse to begin calling police stations and hospitals, then forced herself to be rational.

When Madison didn't answer at seven o'clock the next morning, however, Patrice teetered on the brink of panic. She literally threw on a pair of slacks and dragged a sweater over her head. She wound up her hair, brushed her teeth, and grabbed a piece of dry toast. Finally she surrendered to the inanimate object that had now become her enemy. She asked information for the number of Virginia Brannen.

"Miss Harrows. How nice to hear from you," Virginia said in her reasonable, steady voice. "Is something wrong?"

"Ah . . ." Now Patrice didn't know how to keep from sounding like a scheming female. "I need to get in touch with Madison on a matter, Mrs. Brannen," she said with strained tranquillity. "I think he must be out of town."

The silence on the other end did not reassure her.

"No-o." Virginia drew out the word as if she knew things she were not telling. "He didn't say anything about leaving. Of course, things have been pretty bad since the trouble over Miles."

"Trouble?"

"Didn't he tell you?" The pause was awkward. "Oh, I'm sorry, Miss Harrows. I naturally assumed he would say something to you. Madison's a closed man sometimes. I—"

Patrice had had enough experience in deductive reasoning to guess pretty well what had happened. "You mean, he did go through with the petition?"

"Oh, yes. I hated to see it. But when your children grow up, there's not a lot you can do. You love them both, and . . . well, that's my problem. I don't mean to dump it on your shoulders."

Repeatedly rubbing at her forehead, Patrice was anxious to go now. Madison had undoubtedly lost his appeal for custody, but she said the words anyway. "Madison didn't get custody, did he?"

"I understand why he tried. Rose isn't the best mother in the world, but she is the boy's mother." Virginia's torn grief laced thickly through her words. "Even when Madison was a little boy he was so tenderhearted, things upset him. When he sees that boy do without . . . well, I understand why he did it."

Patrice forced an optimism she was far from feeling. "Mrs. Brannen, I don't know what Madison has told you about our friendship." Before Virginia could reply, Patrice hurried on. "I care what happens to Madison, Mrs. Brannen. If you think it's all right, I'll try to find him. I figure he's just low right now. Maybe he's ducked out of sight to lick his wounds."

"If you find him, would you tell him to call me? He was so low when he talked to me last. . . ."

"If he doesn't, I'll call you myself. Please don't worry."

Virginia's laugh was maternally ironic. "Don't

worry? I'm afraid that's asking the sun to not come up, my dear."

Hands trembling, angry now that Madison had been so callous as to let them worry about him, Patrice wound up the conversation. After a quick call to Adam Wentworth saying she would check in later, and along with many misgivings, she drove to Madison's house.

Patrice had never been to Madison's house before. He had talked about it, and it was everything he said it was—a charming older home that had been renovated and bricked, occupying a corner lot in an older, restricted area of town where real estate values were scandalously high. The yard was ankle deep in fallen leaves, painting the lawn a gorgeous orange and scarlet and rust. She tromped through them, taking a vigorous breath of their pungency, and rang the doorbell.

The doorbell got no better results than the telephone.

Neither did the knocker when she slammed it.

She peeped inside the garage. His pickup was parked there, and a new-model compact car. In the backyard, which was surrounded by a wooden fence, a splendid setter sat on her haunches and curiously observed Patrice reach inside for the clasp of the gate.

"Hello, girl," Patrice said heedfully, creaking the gate open several inches. "I do hope you like people. Nice, nice doggie." The dog advanced, sniffed at Patrice's timidly offered fingertips, then wagged her tail. Patrice scratched her ears.

"How like Madison you are," she mused. "So trusting. Well, girl, where is the man about the house? You have water and food, so I venture he's not too far away." She warily mounted the back steps and tried the back door. Much to her surprise she found it unlocked.

She gave the setter a sheepish apology and pushed it open. Her eyes widened with amazement. The laundry room was a living mess! She almost feared to go any farther. Madison was a fastidious man, and to find a situation so uncharacteristic alerted her to expect the worst. She reached the kitchen door and tried it, too.

"You certainly don't lock up after yourself, Madison," she muttered, entering the house.

After seeing the laundry room, the catastrophe of the house wasn't such a shock. Dirty dishes filled the sink and cluttered the countertops. The garbage hadn't been taken out in days. From the kitchen to the living room wound a trail of scattered newspapers, empty beer cans, a half-empty wine bottle and dirty clothes.

"Oh, Madison!" she breathed, consumed with a sudden rush of guilt. "What has happened to you?"

She dreaded opening his bedroom door. She called out first. "Madison, it's Patrice. Are you in there?"

Silence. Then the hushed rustle of a movement.

Taking a fortifying breath, finding her courage sadly depleted, she shoved open the door.

In the darkness of the room she could see very little. She didn't need to see; she could feel his stillness, his despair. Oh, God! Her poor, poor Madison!

He lay facedown on the bed, the contours of his back naked and brown above his cutoff jeans. It wasn't such a strong back now, only broad and tired and vulnerable. Instinctively she bent to touch it. But then she thought better of it and straightened. Easing herself down, she prudently positioned herself beside his waist.

"Madison?" she whispered. She gently shook his shoulder. "Wake up. You can't stay here like this any longer. Get up."

He moaned into the pillow. When he roused enough to realize she was really there, he made a sound of embarrassed refusal and buried his unshaved face in the pillow. "I'll be all right. Go away."

"No."

"I don't want you to see me like this. Go away. I'll . . . just go away."

She didn't argue with him. She rose and began

gathering his dirty clothes from the floor and placing them outside the door. She opened the venetian blinds and sent sunshine exploding through the room.

His muffled resentment growled from the pillow. One knee drew upward to his chin, and he scoured a hand across the stubbled face in an effort to clear away the fog. Then he rolled over. Gradually his eyes, bloodshot and glazed, focused on her as she stood at the foot of his bed.

"How'd you get in?" he demanded.

"Through the door, klutzie. You look terrible."

The vague hint of a smile passed across his lips, and he squeezed his eyes tightly shut.

"Aren't you answering your telephone these days?" she asked, then walked to the cord running from the wall to his bedside table. It lay disconnected. Stooping, she plugged it back into the outlet. "Your mother's worried about you. It's very selfish of you, you know, to drive us all crazy, wondering if you were sick or in some jail somewhere."

He scowled at her. "Get off my case, counselor."

The corners of her mouth turned downward. "Someone needs to get on your case. Get in the shower, and I'll make coffee."

Sitting for a moment, he slumped back on the pillows. For a second she thought he had passed out. Her eyes dropped to his bare legs. She remembered kissing them, running her parted lips down them, caressing the uneven scars on his knees. Now part of her almost hated him because she was standing here, suffering over him.

When he flung an arm over his eyes, Patrice hardly knew where to begin with him. He was such a complex man. How did one comfort a man so tender, someone who had lived through so many horrors yet was devastated over a small boy?

Like an uncertain beginner, she bent over him to smooth back the locks that tumbled over his forehead.

Even that fragile caress seemed to break some tautly stretched nerve in him. He dragged his arm over his eyes, and she looked down at the tears sparkling there. Her heart wrenched.

"I made a mistake," he said. "I wanted to make things better, but I made a mistake."

She wasn't certain who reached out for whom. But it really didn't matter. Madison raised himself up, opening his arms, and drew her down to him. He turned his face into the comfort of her neck. He held her to him as if she were medicine to his sore, aching heart. His tears drizzled over her shoulder.

"Loving is never a mistake, Madison," she said tenderly and cupped her hand about the back of his head. "Sometimes it gets misplaced and hurts the ones we least intend it to. But it's never a mistake."

His words were contorted with his loss. "I swore, years ago in Nam, that I would never be the source of pain for another human being as long as I lived. Look at me. Rose took the boy. Now none of us knows where he is. Or how he is."

"Shh. I'm sure he's all right. You have to have faith about some things, Madison. You came through Vietnam alive for some purpose. Miles needs you. You just have to be patient and be there for him. Whatever and however that is."

Patrice had never had a man cling to her for strength before. She couldn't remember anyone clinging to her for anything. Being needed so honestly was humbling. She felt as if part of her were knitting to him, like two bones into one, two pieces of flesh into one body. It was terrifying to feel so close to another human being. When the feeling went away, what did one do with the emptiness that was left?

She couldn't bear to think about that so she drew herself away and said briskly, "Come on, into the shower with you. We'll both feel better when we get a cup of something hot."

Letting out his breath in a long ragged sigh, straightening the leg that had been folded beneath him, he studied her for a moment as she stood in the doorway. He knew he looked terrible. He felt terrible. His knees hurt, and his head was near to shattering. He was embarrassed for having let her see him cry.

He blotted at the moist residue below his eyes. "Why did you come?" he asked hoarsely.

Patrice adjusted her sweater about her waist. She found it impossible to meet the raw truth in his bleary eyes.

"Because you needed me," she said simply and walked out of the room.

By the time Patrice had made a sizable dent in the disorder of Madison's kitchen, he ambled into the sun-filled room. He wore a fresh pair of cutoff jeans with his clean shirt unbuttoned, his face freshly shaved, pale as death itself. On his feet were the familiar sneakers.

Since she was so uncertain about the mixture of feelings that spun about in her head, she concentrated on the scrambled eggs and poured him a cup of coffee.

"Have you eaten at all the last few days?" she asked, her eyes pointedly remaining on the place mat, the napkin, the silver, then the toaster as it popped up.

Madison made one of those male noises meant to be taken either way. "You're beautiful," he said and stepped behind her to wrap his arms about her waist. His hands invariably moved upward to mold about her breasts.

She promptly dropped the toast, retrieved it and began buttering it furiously. "I didn't come for you to tell me that." She moved from his nuzzling embrace and placed the toast on the table.

The chair scraped on the floor as Madison slumped down onto it and tested the steaming coffee. "What did you really come for?" he asked. "And don't give me that hype about my needing you."

She spun around to face him, her shoulders reprimanding. "You did need me."

When she placed the toast in front of him, he bit into a piece with a crunch. "That's true," he admitted. "But?"

His gaze flicked over her, and he suddenly grinned. His smile was such a welcome sight, Patrice smiled back. Then they laughed nervously. The old pains were gradually fading into the past.

"Shouldn't you be at work?" His fingers flipped toward her slacks and tennis shoes.

"I am working. Do you think cleaning up after you is play? I've taken the day off."

"Ah," he said. "So you could take care of the poor and needy."

"The needy, at any rate."

He glanced about himself, then ran his fingers through his damp hair. "I've brushed my teeth," he said. "You want to get married now?"

Though he said it in fun, lightly and off-the-cuff, Patrice knew exactly what he had done. He had deliberately brought them back to the same impasse where they had parted so bitterly before. There was nothing inconsistent about Madison Brannen!

She gave him her answer in the same teasing fashion. "You don't need a wife, Madison. You need a live-in maid. Shall I pack my suitcase?"

Madison took several bites of his eggs and laid down his fork. "I think this is where I came in," he remarked cryptically. She knew what he meant.

He walked to the counter and poured himself another cup of coffee. Seeing her empty cup, he filled it, too. He extended it to her and gestured to the chair opposite him.

Patrice declined to sit. She searched through his cupboards and discovered the box of garbage sacks. Ripping one off, she flipped it open with a resounding pop. Bending, she began cramming trash into it.

165

"I don't see how one man can do so much damage," she rambled.

He was standing right behind her. "Miles is out of the picture now," he said. "You can't accuse me of *needing* a wife."

"You take better care of your dog than you do of yourself," she scolded under her breath.

"Patrice?"

"You need a keeper, leaving your door unlocked, cutting yourself off from the world. . . ."

Madison snatched the garbage bag from her hand and flung it away with a majestic flourish.

"Will you put that damned thing down?"

He captured her as she attempted to dart away. Pinning both arms to her sides, he forced her so immutably still she was compelled to look up at him. A sudden shiver passed through her as she tumbled into the depths of his blue eyes.

"Believe me when I say this," he gritted between his teeth. "I once told you I wouldn't beg. I'm not begging now. But I love you. I want to marry you. I want to have children. We could have a good life. Much better than most."

She let her eyes close when what she really wanted to do was lean against him, to feel his arms about her. But he wouldn't stop at just holding, she knew.

"I wasn't joking when I said I'd move in here." She moaned brokenly. "But marriage? And babies? Oh God, Madison, why do you ask for the one thing I can't give you?"

The only part of him that relented was the grip of his fingers on her arms. She heard him breathing. He wasn't nearly as steady as he pretended to be.

"I ask it because you love me."

When the truth fell, it plummeted with a crash. Patrice felt the insane need to cry, to run away, to scream. She pushed away from him and walked rapidly to the living room where she had placed her handbag.

She snatched it up and collided with him when she whirled around.

He refused to let her pass, filling the doorway with his body.

"Let me by."

"Not until you admit the truth to me. You owe me that much."

"I don't owe you anything, Madison Brannen!"

"You owe me for a Kawasaki, and several months of sleepless nights, darling. You owe me because you've ruined my life. Do you think I can ever be happy again without you? Oh yes, you owe me, my darling."

"No!" she cried and walked straight to the wall and dropped her forehead against it and wished she had never come. This man had the most devastating way of getting inside her.

She felt his fingers bury into the thickness of her hair. She felt him lifting out the pins and letting it fall down her back and shaking it loosely about her shoulders. Then he brushed it from her neck and kissed the vulnerable curve of her nape.

"Tell me," he groaned and buried his face in the silky mass. "I want to hear you say it."

"I care very much for you. More than I should."

The heat of his breath and his legs straining against hers were doing strange things to her knees. If she weren't already slumped against the wall, he would have had to hold her up.

"That's not enough," he urged. "Tell me why you came."

"I was worried."

"Why were you worried?"

The sob bubbled up into her throat. She pressed her arms hard over her breasts. They ached. She ached all over. "Because . . . oh, damn it, Madison, because I love you."

"Then marry me."

Her answer was a breath. "I can't."

"What *can* you do?" His voice was hoarse with frustration.

Turning in his arms as naturally as a flower to the sun, standing on tiptoe, she twined her arms about his neck and brushed her lips across his. She pressed her mouth to his ear, begging him to understand even more of her.

"I can love you, Madison. I swear I do, and I've tried not to." Her lips sought the line of his jaw. She was pleading with him, whispering. "I want you, Madison. You're the only man I've ever wanted like this." Now she was trembling. "Just take me as I am. Love me. Now. Please."

Her hands cradled the back of his head. Madison choked a hoarse, guttural sound as her tiny, darting tongue met his. Lowering to his waist, her arms circled him. Her hands slipped boldly below the loose band of his jeans, beneath the top of his briefs, smoothing his hips with her palms. As their mouths clung with a hungry fierceness she pressed herself to him like fragile gossamer against warm, dark earth.

"I'm tired of pretending," she confessed against the nakedness of his chest. "I've got years of love saved up for you, Madison."

Her kisses began to drift across his collarbone, the strong span of muscles, the wisps of curling hair. She grew reckless with need and buried her fingers deep into the leanness of his buttocks, cutting into his flesh with her nails.

Madison ached with desire. He had always wanted this from her. He felt her hands shake as they moved to the front of his jeans, unbuttoning them. He heard the whisper of his zipper, and he didn't doubt her intentions for a moment, nor the fact that she loved him. But he didn't want an affair with her. He wanted everything. A few moments of ecstasy, even her sublime adoration, was not enough. It had to be forever.

He detached himself from her willing arms and lowered them to her sides. "You don't know what you're doing, Patrice. You have no idea."

"I'm not a child," she said, hesitating.

He shook his head. "No, not a child. A woman who's been hurt, and who's afraid to trust."

For a moment she stared at him, stung with disbelief that he could be refusing the most precious thing she had to offer. Defeated in a way she didn't dream was possible, her head jerked aside and her hair swirled about her. "I'm not afraid," she choked when she was terrified of what she had done.

She twisted back suddenly, and her eyes flashed with scorn. *"You're* afraid."

He drew down one corner of his mouth. "Yes, I'm afraid."

The pain he had inflicted glistened brightly in her eyes. He grabbed at her hands. He held them fast and moved his lips to her ear. He was desperate to make her understand.

"I want to wake up with you beside me in the mornings, sweetheart. I want to come home to you. I want to build myself around you. Yes, I'm so afraid of not having that, I—"

Her whole body went stiff with hurt as she froze in his arms. He could literally feel her detach herself from him, though she didn't move. Her fury, when he looked at her, was complete—an unsheathed blade, murderously dangerous.

"You want?" she said icily. *"You want?* What about what I want?" She spun away from him.

"What are you going to do when you're older, Patrice?" he asked suddenly panicking. "What're you going to do when you're sick, when your hair isn't so sparkling and your face isn't as soft?"

When he reached for her she shrank as a hurt animal cowers from that which would injure it. His voice grew raspy with urgency. A confusion like nothing he had ever known diffused over him. "Patrice, I want you so much I think I'm dying, but—"

"No you don't. You want your idea of what it should be like. I'm really sorry to have embarrassed you, Madison."

Refusing to let him see the enormity of her grief, Patrice retrieved her bag from where it had dropped to the floor. She didn't know he reached for her when she stooped. Nor did she see the regret dull his gaze, for she never looked back. Never had she felt so totally humiliated, so utterly like a fool, so miserably rejected, in all her life. And she had said she loved him!

Lord help her, it was the truth; she did love him. So she didn't know where to go except out of this house. She was very careful to lock the gate when she left.

Madison didn't watch her go. That was one defeat he couldn't observe. So he sat with his head buried in his hands and wished he could begin again with her. He had made so many mistakes with her. But he was only a man. How was he to know the entirety of another person's heart?

There was one thing he did know, however. One of them was going to change some aspects about the institution of marriage. He didn't know how and he didn't know when. But it would happen someday, and it wouldn't be him.

The need to talk to someone troubled Patrice. Rarely had she ever reached this point, but rarely had she ever hurt this badly. Betty was the worst possible choice for confidences because she thought only in terms of appearances. Cathy was too busy with her own marital problems to put her mind to anything else. Upon occasion she had discussed problems with Adam, but never anything as catastrophic as this.

The only other person she could go to was her father.

Confiding in Simon Clayburne was a risk. They had never shared truly intimate things. But they were older and wiser now, as the saying went. Perhaps this one time he could be a father. She had to try.

When she arrived at the Atlantis II, it was a week before the gala opening. Everything was a mass of disorganization. The decorators were putting the finishing touches on the mirrors and furnishings. Electrical equipment was strewn everywhere, and the carpet people appeared to be on the verge of tight-lipped hysteria trying to work around it.

Even when she had lived at home, Patrice didn't go to her father's office. This particular casino was a posh hotel, stylish, and would be frequented by some of the best clientele in the country. But the Clayburne women never visited the casinos—a sort of unspoken law, she supposed.

A man at the door, whose western boots, jeans, and hat could not disguise the fact that he was a security guard, directed her to a temporary office beyond the blackjack tables. She weaved around huge rolls of unlaid carpeting and waited outside the door for a moment. Was this such a good idea, after all?

As she posed her hand to knock, the door opened.

Simon Clayburne stepped out into the vast spaces of his new domain. He was a striking man, flanked by two other men, one who resembled an assistant, another who was obviously an architect by the rolls of designs tucked under his arm.

At the unexpected sight of his daughter, Simon stopped short. Placing a hand on the shoulder of the assistant, he nodded and gestured with his eyes as if the man would automatically know what to do.

"Honey!" he exclaimed jovially and wrapped his arm about Patrice's shoulders. He hugged her energetically. "What're you doing down here? I thought you'd be slaving away at that job of yours. Everything going well? You keeping law and order in this land of ours? Reading all those shelves of books with leather covers?"

Smiling, wishing he wouldn't belittle her job, Patrice hugged her father back. "Being a lawyer isn't quite like they show in the movies, Daddy."

Simon was a tall man, immaculately suited, silver-haired. His large hands were well tended, and the extra weight the years had given him was becomingly distributed. He looked like the epitome of prosperity, which he was.

"I'm on a long lunch hour," Patrice explained, feeling as if she were interrupting. "Could I invite you out? I'm buying, of course."

He chuckled at her mock generosity. "I'd love to, sweetie, but all hell's broken loose around here. Now the decorator's telling me we'll be two days late opening, when I thought we'd be a day early. I'll have to take a rain check on the lunch. But soon, huh?"

She smothered her disappointment in a smile. "Sure, Dad."

As if it just dawned on Simon how strange it was for his older daughter to come downtown to the casino, he gnawed at the inside of his lip, frowning. "Are you sure you're all right? Is something the matter?" His frown disappeared, and he began fishing in his hip pocket for his wallet. "Ah, I get it. How much do you need?"

Her dismay was a physical thing, nauseous. She grabbed his arm quickly. "No, Daddy. Honestly, I don't need money. I just wanted to—"

Across the room a technician waved at Simon. Grabbing both her arms, squeezing them without even looking at the anguish clouding her eyes, he said, "Wait right here. This'll just take a minute."

She watched the sight of his back. She had watched him do this all her life. Simon Clayburne was known, commonly speaking, as a wheeler-dealer. She didn't know what arrangements he had with his associates, nor his standing with the Internal Revenue Service. She doubted that Betty knew any more than she did. They had all spent the money he made and asked no questions. Except her. Since her divorce, she refused all financial support.

"I'm sorry, honey," Simon's return snapped Patrice back to the present. He guided her into the open door and removed a cigarette from a pack. Before he lit it the telephone began ringing. "Damn," he muttered, shrugging sheepishly.

Patrice gave him a gentle shove toward the makeshift desk in the corner. "Answer your phone, Daddy."

He lifted the receiver and cupped it in his palm. "It won't take but a minute. Come on in. Find something to sit on. Sorry about the mess. This is only a storage room."

As he began talking business she stood in the doorway and observed the bustle going on outside. It had been a bad idea to come. Simon wasn't a bad man. He only had time to do one thing: make money. She had forgotten what it had been like, all those years of growing up, never seeing him, not really knowing him.

Simon glanced upward, pausing, as if he just remembered her presence. "Ah . . . I can't right now, Jack. I have someone in the office."

The disappointment Patrice felt didn't surprise her, and she despised the thickening knot in her throat. What the heck? she scolded herself. How could she tell her father, "Daddy, I offered myself to the only man I've ever loved and he didn't want me?"

She held up her palms, indicating for him to not change his plans on her account. "I have to go," she whispered loudly.

Reluctantly, Simon shook his head. "Yes, Jack," he said, "but—"

Stepping to Simon's side, she laid her hand on the expensive sleeve of his suit. "I can come back," she said. "Really."

"Hold on, Jack," he said, then covered the receiver with his palm. "I didn't mean to get tied up the minute you got here, Patty."

She pasted a smile on her face. What else could she have expected?

"I insist," she said energetically.

"But you didn't even tell me why you came."

The laugh she tossed over her shoulder was almost painful. "To wish you good luck, Daddy. And that's what I wish you." She blew him a kiss. "I'll read about my famous father in the *Telegram*. Tell Mother I said hello."

Scowling, shifting in his chair, Simon replaced the receiver to his ear. He uttered some incoherent apology into the mouthpiece. He glanced up just as Patrice reached the door.

Feeling the thrust of tears welling behind her eyes, she waved at him. Before she was out the door Simon was deeply ensnarled in technicalities with Jack. She slumped against the wall outside the room. What was she doing wrong that everyone turned from her?

She covered her eyes for a moment, then removed her hands to find two men pausing in their work to stare at her. She walked swiftly across the long room and out the door.

Once on the sidewalk she leaned back to view the hotel as it pierced the sky like a great steel needle. Money would come through these doors and flow across these tables. Well, people said there were two things that kept the world going around—money and love. Out of pride she had bravely, and impersonally, refused the first.

Why had she refused the second with Madison? Stupidity, she decided, walking tiredly to her car. Downright stupidity.

When the call came, Patrice was standing in her office, balancing precariously in a chair, flipping over a

174

page on a huge decorator calendar. *April,* read the elaborate cursive script. *Spring,* the month of Easter. Six months had passed since she had made the fumbling attempt to confide in her father.

Five of those months, she recalled bleakly, had been spent trying to recover from her infatuation with Madison Brannen. The last month had been tolerable, if not happy. She had done it; she had learned how to go on living without him.

Randy Newberry, the eager-beaver office clerk, poked his head inside her office at the exact instant her telephone began buzzing. "Quick, pick it up!" he said.

Patrice arched her brows high at his eighteen-year-old enthusiasm and climbed down off the ladder. She brushed at the seat of her gray wool slacks. Tugging off her clip earring, she watched Randy as she told the operator to put through the call.

"Yes, this is Mrs. Harrows."

The voice at the other end of the line was nearly drowned out by the sound of a siren screaming past. A siren had its own connotations for Patrice. Madison's bearded face flashed before her mind's eye, and for a split second she was back in the ambulance with him bending over her, holding her hands.

"What is it?" Her voice quivered. "I can't hear you!"

"An explosion, Mrs. Harrows," came the winded reply of a voice she knew she should recognize.

"Mr. Potter?" she asked with a chilling presentiment. "Rawlins, is that you?"

"Yes. I think you should get up here, Mrs. Harrows. Some dummy has blown up half the Remcon plant. Everything's a crazy mess."

Another siren shrieked past. Patrice believed him without question, and a cold horror made her numb all over. "Rawlins," she said, almost afraid to ask, "are there injuries?"

"A few," he yelled over the noise. "Nothing really serious. At least no one's dead. But Remcon is positive

175

that some loony from Bridgeport set the dynamite. Or plastic explosives, who knows? They have their lawyer up here, and the police are pouring in."

"*Did* someone at Bridgeport set it off?"

"Probably. Hell, I don't know. I think you'd better come."

Patrice waved aside the overeager questions Randy was bursting to ask. With the telephone receiver pinched under her jaw, she had already begun cramming things into her attaché case.

"Yes, Rawlins. I'm on my way. For heaven's sake, see if you can get a list of the injuries. Tell the official in charge I'm driving up. If they're taking statements, the Bridgeport employees ought to wait until I get there before they say anything."

"You got it. And hurry."

Randy blasted her with questions the moment she set the receiver down. Answering what she could, she raced for her jacket. Then she cut him off with a gesture.

"Find out where Adam is," she ordered, "and tell him I've gone to Bridgeport." On her way out the door she turned. "Oh, yes, and phone my sister. Tell her I'm out of town in case anyone tries to reach me."

"Yes, ma'am," the crestfallen clerk agreed. He had hoped to be asked along.

Patrice could hardly think of anything as she drove upstate. Had Madison been hurt? Even though the construction was nearing completion, she was certain he and his men were still up there. In spite of her butchered pride she had found out that much.

Oh, Patrice, stop thinking this way! Madison Brannen is past history. Grow up!

The construction site was a seething mess. Fire trucks and police cars flashed their lights. Ambulances raced in and out along the newly paved road. She had to park the Ferrari far away from the scene. The television, predictably enough, had gotten wind of the industrial sabotage; their crew was on duty.

One of the first people she spotted once she neared the confusion was Rawlins Potter. She shook his offered hand absently, glancing on both sides of her to assess the damage.

"Glad you could come," he said and fit a clipboard beneath his arm.

"Did you get a list of the injured?"

"Just a partial one. It's mostly burns. A beam fell on a few guys and some got hurt with pieces of flying glass."

Without admitting to herself what she was actually doing, Patrice frantically scanned the list for Madison's name. She slumped with relief when she didn't find it.

Phil Anthony, the last person Patrice wanted to tangle with just now, spotted her. Detaching himself from a group of Remcon men, mostly technicians, he strode over, his face a darkened thundercloud.

"Well, well, counselor," he rumbled sarcastically. "Seems like your children have been misbehaving, doesn't it?"

Patrice kept her face a blank mask. "Quite a deduction, Mr. Anthony. I trust you've found evidence to back that up."

He jammed a finger beneath the tip of her nose. "What I need, I'll find, lady. We'll drag in every man and his dog for questioning on this one. You can take that to the bank. And speaking of banks, do you know what this lunacy is going to cost?"

"If you don't behave rationally, Mr. Anthony, you may find yourself tied up with false arrest charges as well." She smiled placidly. "Perhaps someone on your own staff saw an easy way out of this controversy and decided a healthy insurance settlement was the way to go. Hmm?"

The man's gray eyes narrowed maliciously. "Don't

give me that whitewashed garbage. This was no inside job and you know it."

"No, I do not know that, Mr. Anthony. Was anyone hurt that I know?"

Anthony's forced smile turned into something closer to a leer. "You mean Brannen? A scratch. Nothing more. What happened between you two. I thought you and he . . ." He let his words trail off suggestively.

The muscles in Patrice's face hardened. Her underlying resiliency flashed through. "Take it somewhere and scrap it, Mr. Anthony!" She was furious. "Get out of my way."

"You can't go over there." He jabbed a thumb in the direction of the shambles.

"Watch me!"

For the next two hours Patrice listened to accounts of the incident from the Bridgeport employees who wanted to speak with her. Madison was far back in her mind as ambulances transferred the wounded out of the area and a paramedic unit treated the minor injuries on the site. Where was Madison? Was he all right? Would she see him? Oh, God, did she want to see him?

When she finished taking the last statement and setting up the last appointment, she ambled toward the still-smoking area of the explosion. Meticulously she picked her way around the fringes of broken glass and twisted metal. Whoever had done this was no novice, she figured; it could hardly have done more damage.

One of the fire trucks was winding up its hose, and, nodding at one of the firemen, she walked behind it. Emerging from behind the truck and glancing toward a heavy-equipment crew beginning to commence with the worst of the cleanup, Patrice stopped in her tracks.

Not fifty yards away, wearing a hard hat, his khakis filthy with soot and one sleeve torn open to the edge of his insulated vest, stood Madison. He was peering up at a bulldozer operator. One booted foot was braced on a pedestal, and he pointed to a smoking pile of wreckage.

His bandage, no longer white, was stained with dried blood. As if he were drawn by her presence, his eyes swept methodically over the wreckage. With his arm still outstretched, his gaze came to rest on her.

Everything vanished for the two of them: the noise, the confusion, the destruction. For six months they had not seen each other, had not spoken. Even so, it could have been six hours or six minutes, or no time at all.

Neither could move. Neither could tear their eyes away. And then Patrice felt the cutting edge of the truth. She wasn't over anything. Time couldn't separate her from Madison Brannen. Nothing ever could.

Chapter Nine

*T*here had once been a time when Patrice had scoffed at the lyrics of songwriters and the rhymes of poets. "Time stood still," they said. She had thought it was nothing but a pretty play on words up until the moment it happened to her. And it happened in the most unexpected, most noisy, confused place she could have imagined—Bridgeport, New Jersey, at the site of a multimillion-dollar disaster.

From his side of the destruction site Madison was only one man among many. But out of that confusion time did stand still.

You came, he said without words.

I've missed you, her look told him.

Madison finally regained his ability to move. Without looking, he yelled an order to the equipment operator near him. Then he began picking his way through twisted steel toward her.

Over the roar of the machinery, the operator shouted a question, but Madison didn't hear it. His eyes were riveted immutably to hers. Patrice didn't think anything could have prevented him from coming to her.

For a moment, as Madison reached her, his lips toyed with a wondering smile. His gaze, startlingly blue in his dirty face, greedily devoured everything about her as if he were making up for the months they had been apart.

"How've you been?" he asked at last. His words came out rusty and broken. Coughing lightly, he wiped a hand over his face, which only tended to smear the grime. He removed his hard hat with the same movement and raked his fingers through his hair.

As if she expected someone to be observing them, Patrice glanced about herself. She moistened her lips nervously. "Fine," she said and nodded, smiling. "Fine. I've been keeping busy."

Another fire truck shrieked past. Madison replaced his bright yellow hat and watched the truck lumber into position.

"And you?" she prompted.

His attention snapped back to her. "Ahh, I've been doing okay, too. Most of the time."

He lifted his shoulders as if he were tempted to say something more, then dropped them. His grin pulled one corner of his mouth down. "I've been spending a lot of time out here. You can't tell it now, though."

Their awareness of the other increased, raw and acute and stinging. Neither knew how much or what to say.

Presently Madison shifted his weight. Patrice, forgetting for a moment where she was, reached out in an automatic gesture to inspect the wound on his arm. Remembering the last time she had touched him, she snatched back her hand. She placed it with her other about the handle of her attaché case, but not before he saw that she was trembling.

His fingers absently rubbed the soiled gauze wrapping.

181

"Is that . . . okay?" she asked in a high voice.

He peered over at it, then dismissed it. "Yeah. A cut."

"Oh."

"It's not much. I'll get a few stitches later."

"Are you sure it's okay?"

He grinned wanly. "I'm sure."

She sighed heavily, then looked around herself again, not seeing anything except the memories of him nestled to her breast, of him pinning her against the wall of his mother's old washroom.

"Madison—"

"Patrice—"

They both smiled, and slowly, as they felt their feet sinking into the old familiar quicksand they both sobered again.

The need to ask him if any of it had mattered, if he still thought of it, was breaking Patrice's heart. And Madison, compelled to do something with his hands before he hugged her until she couldn't breathe, tugged a handkerchief from his hip pocket and wiped his hands.

"Have you heard from Miles?" she questioned abruptly. She didn't want to talk about Miles.

"He's still with his mother. Things aren't perfect, but . . ." His smile dwindled awkwardly and he replaced the handkerchief. "But things are never perfect, are they?"

This was much more painful than Patrice would have imagined it to be. She studied her shoes. One toe was blackened with soot. A long smudge streaked down the left side of her pink skirt. She unconsciously flicked at it.

"No," she replied, then felt the burning scald of tears. Oh, Lord help her! She couldn't go to pieces now.

She lifted her head with the instinctive elegance Madison had watched so often. His ability to read her thoughts had not lessened with the passing of time. He knew, as he always knew, that she was hurting.

His fingers closed about the wrist of her hand that was brushing aimlessly at a pleat in her skirt. They both gasped, and when she ceased pulling away, he lifted her hand gently. He fit her small palm against his upturned one, aligning their fingers, then studying them as if nothing else in the world mattered.

Patrice could hardly breathe.

"I still love you," he said with such hoarse tenderness that her defenses melted like ice in the sun.

She swallowed hard, then again. "Don't make me cry."

"I never meant to make you cry." Over the noise his words were hardly audible. "I swear to God. Never."

In a gesture meant to stop his apology—for their parting had been more her fault than his—she waved her hand. She spoke quickly.

"Madison, Mother is giving a sort of lawn party next week. It's probably the type of thing you hate, but if you'd suffer through it . . . I mean, just for a few—" She groped for words.

"I would like very much to come," he said, smiling. "Black tie?"

Her eyebrows lifted. She suddenly felt enormously happy. She laughed breathlessly. "Yes. Mother never does anything unless it can make the magazine section of the Sunday paper."

The lines about Madison's eyes crinkled, leaving faint, pale tracks in the grime. He could have been touching her, she thought; he could have been kissing her.

Behind him someone shouted. "Hey, Brannen!"

"I have to go," he said reluctantly.

The smile she gave him felt like the first time she had smiled in six months. "You'll get an invitation from Mother," she said and refused to think about wheedling Betty into doing it.

As she walked numbly to her car she pivoted to find him watching her leave. One of his hands unconsciously held his bandaged arm. Lifting the fingers of one hand level with her jaw, she waved them with the delicacy of a leaf fluttering in a breeze.

He didn't wave back, but he smiled. He settled his hard hat on his head and returned to the grim task of repairing what had taken so long to build. She looked at him only once again. He had stepped onto the bulldozer and was surveying the smoking ruins. How had he managed to steal her heart away. How had he managed to make her love him?

The huge Clayburne house was undergoing a vigorous cleaning when Patrice pushed open the front door and called for her mother. Over the roar of the vacuum cleaners inside and the lawn crews mowing outside, she could hardly make herself heard.

A lawn party was a yearly ritual for Betty, and a minimum of two fully staffed cleaning teams worked through both stories of the Tudor-style mansion. In one week's time not a blade of grass would be left untended on the spacious ten acres. Not one carpet or drape would go untended. Hurricane lamps would be cleaned and positioned alongside the dramatic, winding drive. The veranda canopy would be erected and tables and chairs newly scrubbed. The pool house would be renovated from top to bottom.

The chamber ensemble that would be hired would be paid extremely well. The photographer would earn enough on this one event to cover a month's expenses. None of Simon's colorful associates would be invited, but all of Betty's well-to-do friends would attend. It would be, as always, the event of the season.

Betty was descending the curved staircase as Patrice strode through the house searching for her.

"Darling, what are you doing here this time of day?" Betty smoothed her slacks and shirt, managing to look like a model even in her cleaning clothes, and stepped gracefully to the landing.

Patrice laughed. "I'm here to get a status report, Mother. How many last-minute emergencies have you had so far?"

"Only two. Allen is overseas photographing some silly little twit's wedding. I'm going to be forced to make do with Ruthie. And you know what a terrible photographer that woman is."

"Ruth is a fine photographer. She's just not a good diplomat."

As Betty made her way to the breakfast room, issuing a barrage of orders right and left as she went, Patrice ambled behind her. What would Madison think of this house? she wondered. That it was pretentious? Yes, and then he would understand why everyone had called her a "spoiled brat," and why she would rather live in an apartment.

After tugging off a metallic headband, pouring herself a cup of coffee and offering one to Patrice, Betty suddenly paused on her way to the table. She held two cups in her hands. "Goodness, you haven't come to tell me you're not coming, have you?"

Patrice lifted a cup from her mother's hand. "No, Mother. In fact, I want you to send out another invitation. A special favor to me."

"Justin!" The name burst from Betty's lips before she thought. "Oh, darling."

Patrice nearly spilled the coffee. She placed it to the glass-topped table before she ruined her clothes. "No, Mother. Madison Brannen."

Before her mother could launch into a tirade of objections, Patrice's hand came up like a traffic policeman's. "Now, Mother, before you raise a fuss, you know I never ask you for many things. Just this once, please. Do this for me."

As if all her energies had just seeped from her, the older woman dropped to a chair. She sipped from the demitasse cup in silence and focused a decidedly disapproving gaze at her daughter. "Of all the men in the world, Patrice, why do you ask me this?"

Patrice consulted her wristwatch. She hadn't allowed enough time for this battle, she guessed. "Because he's the one I want you to invite, Mother. Do I ask you why you love Daddy?"

"Love? Oh, God, it hasn't come to words like that, has it?" Betty dropped her immaculate head to the heel of her hand. "Patrice, I swear you'll be the death of me. Justin is dying, absolutely *dying* to reconcile, and you—"

"I don't love Justin, Mother. I've never loved Justin."

The Clayburne breakfast room was located in a sunny alcove off the huge formal dining room. Betty's silver coffee service sat impressively beside her white telephone. Beside that was stacked a collection of lists in Betty's elaborate handwriting.

As Patrice sat patiently Betty picked up a gold ballpoint pen and wrote herself another note. Glancing up, she said, "A woman does what she must do, my daughter. Women have done it for centuries. I do it. Your sister does it. Do you think you're exempt?"

Patrice could hardly believe what she was hearing. For the first time in her life she gained an insight into her mother's true feelings about her own marriage, her attitudes toward a relationship between a man and a woman. The tight grimness of Betty's mouth revealed a desperation Patrice had never seen her express.

Her impulse was to go to her mother, to just put her arms about her shoulders. But Betty's pride would never tolerate such a thing. With her, things must be without a flaw. What cruel words passed between Simon and Betty that no one ever knew about?

A cleaning maid stepped into the doorway, and Patrice was jolted back into the reality of where she was. The moment of empathy disappeared as suddenly as it had occurred. It had no past history, no reason for it to linger or to be expressed. A deep sadness hung in the room now. Patrice wanted to leave.

Betty solved the problem. Rising, she dropped her fingertips to her daughter's shoulder. "I'm sorry to interrupt this talk, dear. You can see what I have on my hands."

With unwavering understanding, Patrice closed her hand over her mother's. "But you'll send the invitation to Madison, won't you?"

"I suppose I'll have to. Leave the man's name and address on a card by the telephone. I really have to go now."

"Sure," Patrice replied, feeling disappointed that she and Betty had no common ground. "Call me if I can help."

The glance her mother sent her as Patrice walked toward the door was a strange one. "What?"

Patrice turned back, a question on her face.

"Oh, yes, darling. I will."

Patrice tended to congratulate herself as she steered the Ferrari down the sweeping drive from the mansion. Everything would work out beautifully. She would see Madison again! How could that one fact make her so deliriously happy?

Suddenly she loved the newness of spring, the trees heavy with new leaves, the smell of the air and the street. She forgave Betty for her perpetual distance. She laughed out loud astonishing herself. *She even adored the Ferrari!* Now she only had the problem of finding something to wear that would take Madison's breath away.

For several minutes after Patrice left, Betty sat unmoving at the breakfast table. A frown etched a tiny groove between her brows, and she smoothed it absently. Calmly, decidedly, she withdrew her phone numbers from beneath her lists. She ran a manicured nail down the index until it came to the "H" section. She dialed and waited.

"Hello?" answered a man's voice.

"Justin? This is Betty."

A pause lasted only a fraction of a second. "Betty, how lovely of you to call. Nothing's the matter, is it?"

Betty laughed and sipped her coffee. "Now, what could be the matter, darling? I'm planning my lovely party for all my lovely friends. Which is why I want to extend my invitation to you in person. You will come, won't you?"

Justin hesitated. He sat in a plush office in his home. He didn't often go to the newspaper or his downtown suite. He enjoyed the sybaritic pleasures of his pool and his entourage of young female friends who were willing to share his pleasures for the price of a few hours in his bed.

He dragged on his cigarette. "Aw, Betty, you know I detest all that highbrow music and those fawning matron friends of yours."

Betty's mouth hardened. "They've been rather good to you on occasion, Justin. Besides, Patrice is going to be there."

Justin's feet came off his desk, and he straightened in his chair. He absently took up a pen and began doodling on a pad. "Patrice?"

"Yes, and someone else you might be interested in, Justin. She asked me to invite Mr. Brannen."

A number of impressions formed during the silence. Betty knew her ex-son-in-law well. She knew his pride, and the sharp thorn of his failure to hold Patrice. When Justin let out a heavy sigh, she smiled.

"Brannen, you say?"

"Now be smart, Justin. You've seen the man. This is the perfect opportunity for you to shine beside him. She has succumbed to this infatuation more than once. If she can see the two of you side by side, well . . ."

"Say no more, Betty. I'll be there."

Betty's laughter was rich and full of delicious plans. She was thankful for Justin's high opinion of his own charm. "Wonderful."

"Does Patrice know I'll be there?"

"Let's surprise her, darling. Undoubtedly she'll be miffed, but she's a bright girl. In time, she'll be grateful to both of us. I'm sure that in her heart she still loves you, dear."

Justin stubbed out his cigarette. He wasn't nearly so sure of that as Betty. But Patrice was the only person, or thing, that had ever refused to yield to him. That had stuck in his craw for a long time. This was one time when Madison Brannen would see himself bested right under his nose.

"She's young, Betty. She doesn't know her own mind yet."

"I'm sure you're right."

"Oh." Justin paused before he hung up the telephone. "Since I've been granted such a personal invitation, my dear, call up your favorite florist and give him a free hand. Tell him to send the bill to me."

Betty's eyebrows lifted. Justin rarely disappointed her. "Are you certain, darling?"

"Quite. See you next week."

As a line of clouds moved in over Atlantic City Patrice stood before the windows in her apartment and frowned. Betty Clayburne would simply not tolerate rain at one of her parties. Usually the weather pampered her; today it might not.

Time dragged irritably on her hands. All morning long she had halfheartedly kept to a routine and tried not to fantasize what would happen when she saw Madison again. But she pictured him dancing with her behind the pool house. She imagined him coming up behind her in the hallway and whisking her into one of the bedrooms and kissing her. She heard him say how beautiful she was and how much he adored her.

Feeling foolish, she finally gave up on everything. She dressed hours too early, then had to sit and wait for the hands on the clock to move. Unable to stand the tension, she tromped to the long mirror in her bedroom and, for the dozenth time, gave herself a fastidious inspection.

The price of her floor-length, gold lamé culottes didn't bear remembering. On the foot of her bed lay the swirl of a matching cardigan. To ease her guilty conscience for having spent so much money, she was wearing high-heeled sandals that were several years old. And she had done her own hair. It did look nice, though it had taken her an hour to achieve the "crown" effect she wanted.

Dabbing perfume behind her ears and at her wrists, she glanced at her wristwatch. At last, it was time to go. Another hour of waiting and she would have gone mad. Was he nervous, too?

"My, aren't you handsome?" she told her father when she entered the great house from a side door and found him in the living room before the fireplace. She gave him a daughterly peck on the cheek.

"I inherited my good looks from you, daughter." As Simon chuckled he held her at arm's length and twirled her around, smiling his approval. "Smart," he said. "Very smart."

Remembering the remark Betty had made about her marriage, Patrice steadied herself and drew back a few inches. She seemed to be seeing her father through wise, new eyes. She felt a great need to understand him, where he had come from, his past.

She impulsively took both his hands. "Why is it that we never say 'I love you' enough, Daddy?"

Simon was so surprised that his face fell when he f .iled to remember ever saying such a thing to her. He wasn't a man for demonstrations, and he had never felt that love was particularly important. But Patrice was different today, more womanly, more spiritually touchable. He took her arm and hugged it. It was the most he knew to do.

"I'm glad you're here," Simon said, meaning it. "Your mother's going through her usual travail."

"She's liable to go through more," Patrice answered with a slow smile. "I think it's going to rain."

"Nonsense!" Betty Clayburne stepped up behind them. For a moment her eyes widened as she sensed something new between them. She quickly dismissed it. "It wouldn't dare rain."

Simon snorted at his wife. "Just in case, I've had Carl put fifty folding chairs under the canopy.

Out of courtesy, Patrice stood still as her mother gave her culottes a critical assessment. She lifted her brows for the verdict.

"They're perfect," Betty congratulated her. "Justin will love them."

"What?" Patrice's jaw dropped. "Mother—"

Simon riveted a hard stare upon Betty. "I didn't know Justin was coming, darling."

A scene with her parents was the absolute last thing Patrice wanted. But a scene with Justin would be worse!

She hastily interrupted. "Has Madison gotten here yet?"

Betty looked as if she didn't know what Patrice was talking about. For one heart-stopping moment Patrice thought her mother had forgotten to invite him. And Simon, smelling the familiar scent of trouble, groped inside his suit coat for his cigarettes.

"There seem to be several things I didn't know," he said. His lighter flared, and he angrily snapped it closed.

Betty fluttered her hands. "Oh, you two! Justin is

family. I invited him for myself, not because of you, Patrice. Honestly. And no, I don't think Mr. Brannen has arrived. Perhaps something came up and he couldn't attend. Don't worry about it, darling. We'll have a wonderful time."

Abruptly, discouragingly, the afternoon's silver glitter tarnished. Patrice gazed down at the culottes and remembered the hours of frivolous daydreaming that had gone into them. Standing in this room with the buzz of human gaiety surrounding her, she felt like an idiot, a silly, schoolgirl idiot. She met her father's eyes, and her shoulders, which had drooped for one second of sheer misery, squared. Her jaw tightened in a firm line.

Simon had to stand aside as guests wandered into the house and paused a moment to chat with him. But he didn't miss the transformation of his daughter. Something had died in her, and this wasn't the first time he had seen that look. His habit of cordiality was long practiced, and he smiled at his guests. He called out greetings and laughed at their repartee. But he took the hand of his wife in a rather cruel grip and began drawing her toward the other end of the house.

"I want to talk to you," he said tightly.

Watching them go, Patrice briefly considered leaving the house. How could Betty have done this to her?

But leaving wouldn't solve anything except to make Justin think she was afraid of facing him. She had no sooner walked out onto the lawn than a roving waiter placed a glass of champagne in her hand.

She looked up at him. "Thank you."

"It was a very good year," came a voice from behind her.

A chill riddled through her, and her eyes closed in disbelief. Other than that, she didn't move when she spoke. "Justin, I didn't expect to see you here."

Any feeling of sympathy Patrice cherished for Betty

Clayburne in the preceding days swiftly disappeared as Justin stepped around in front of her. He raked over her attire with wickedly suggestive eyes. And his mouth curved in a sensual, arrogant way. As usual, he looked like a beautiful, innocent boy.

"I'm sure you didn't," he said. "But since I am, put your hand through my arm, my darling, and let's take a stroll over the grounds. For old times' sake. The handsome young husband sporting his gorgeously sexy wife."

"Justin, I wouldn't stroll with you to the car wash. Now get out of my way. I came to enjoy myself."

Justin touched her jaw with a fingertip and drew a line across to her ear and down the curve of her neck. He possessively fondled the gold trim about the neck of her cardigan.

"You're stubborn, unmanageable, have a tongue like a blowtorch—everything I despise in a woman. But I want you back, Patty. I mean to have you back."

"Stop it!"

When she used that tone with him, Justin always ceased playing games. The frivolity in his eyes hardened to its more honest menace. "Only if you behave yourself. Now be a nice baby. Do as I say and I won't embarrass either of us. Fight me, and I'll cause a scene like nothing you ever saw."

"A scene is the last thing you'll cause, Justin. It's taken me three years to learn that. You wouldn't do anything to tilt that halo you flaunt."

In spite of her show of bravery, Patrice knew better than to fight Justin in a public place. From sad experience she knew that he never lost in battles of this sort. So she put what she hoped was a smile on her face and let him walk her over the grounds.

Old friends, from back in their married days, stopped to chat and joke with Justin. Several of the young wives remarked on how well Patrice was looking. Those who knew of her loss of the baby offered their sympathies, and their apologies that they hadn't called or dropped by.

"Are you still working, dear heart?"

"Yes." Patrice maintained her smile.

"Really. How do you stand it?"

"Quite easily. I enjoy it."

"Oh. Well, you and Justin must come down to the Bahamas with us."

"I'm sorry, my schedule just won't permit it right now."

"Oh."

Behind her back gossip spread like fire in a dry meadow.

"Do you suppose those two are getting back together?"

"Well, I never understood why she left him to begin with. All that money!"

"Well, darling, you know the girls Justin has on the side. Maybe she found out."

"What difference does that make, for God's sake? I could work around it."

"Patrice always was too serious about things like that."

"And where did it get her? She's without a man, isn't she? I wouldn't be in her shoes for anything."

Madison dragged a finger beneath his crisp, starched collar and estimated that the Clayburne mansion at the end of the driveway contained over thirty rooms. As he climbed out of the pickup, not exactly the type of automobile being parked along the bricked expanse, he caught the covetous eye of the youthful valet walking toward him.

"Hey, man!" The experienced hot-rod buff whistled as he caught the keys Madison tossed him. "If you ever want to unload that piece of machinery, you got an instant customer."

Two more uniformed young men drew around it, their eyes caressing the truck. They peered inside at the custom leather upholstery. Madison grinned, accustomed to this reaction.

"Hands off, guys," he warned as he buttoned his jacket. "What I've been offered for that you could retire on."

One valet groaned, then narrowed his eyes. "You going in there?" He jabbed a thumb in the direction of the party already in progress.

"Yeah." Madison glanced down at his formal attire, then tugged at his black bow tie. "Aren't I dressed right?"

The valets laughed. "Sure, sure," one said. "You just don't look the type. You got socks on, man?"

Chuckling, Madison left them. He tossed a last warning over his shoulder. "Be careful with that truck."

"Like she was a newborn baby, sir. Get out of the way, Rick, I get to park it."

At the touch of Madison's fingers the heavy front door swept open. Madison gave his name to an austere butler.

"To your right, sir, on the veranda."

The farthest room, whose double doors opened onto a great veranda, was barely visible. Madison received an impression of vast ceilings, luxurious furnishings, and fresh flowers. Though the house managed to convey the flavor of age, he guessed it was less than ten years old. Muted strains of Corelli, blending with laughter and the clink of glassware, reached him even before he glimpsed the coming and going of brightly gowned women and their more somber escorts.

"Just follow your ears, tiger," a sultry voice cooed close behind him. "You can't get lost."

Glancing upward to the curving staircase, Madison smiled back at a tall, willowy brunette as she descended. One hand rested on the banister, and the other adjusted a bright crimson strap that had fallen from her shoulder. From the looks of her, her cocktail hour had begun much earlier. Still, she was lovely.

He grinned and waited for her to reach him. "Thanks. D'you know your way around this place?"

"I'm a fixture at this house. Patrice and I were roommates at college one semester." Without an invitation from Madison, she draped an arm over his shoulder. He could smell the expensive perfume she wore. "I'm Vanessa Rheems. Who are you? I thought I knew all of Betty's regulars."

He shrugged, uncomfortable. "I'm Madison Brannen. And I'm not a regular." He gestured at the spacious affluence surrounding them and wondered where he would find Patrice. "I'm surprised someone hasn't mistaken me for one of the hired help."

"Not with that face, sweetie," Vanessa growled. "Tell me, Madison, are you rich?"

Startled at her nerve, Madison laughed. "No," he drawled. "I'm about the most unrich man you could meet."

Vanessa's face puckered with disappointment, then brightened. "Well, no matter. We can work around it."

Before Madison had time to learn exactly what "working around it" entailed, he was met by the host and hostess. Both of them were so guarded he wasn't certain if they were more uncomfortable with each other or with the sight of Vanessa Rheems clinging to his arm. Betty's aversion, obvious in her murmured aside to Simon and his swift scowl, had not lessened since that day at the hospital.

Madison's affability was only for the sake of Patrice. He wished he was a hundred miles away, fishing by a quiet lake. He stepped forward and extended his hand.

Stiffly smiling, Betty said, "I'm so glad you could come, Mr. Brannen. I see you've already met someone you know." Her nod included Vanessa. "You've found everything, dear?"

The disapproval of the hostess wasn't lost on Vanessa. In a manner that revealed she was accustomed to the language of the very rich, she lifted her brows in a wordless "Well!" and bestowed several pats on Madison's arm. "One of my friends is waving to me. I'll see you later, tiger."

Betty threw her eyes to the ceiling in a regal dismissal, and Madison found that keeping a straight face was a test of control. He didn't move a muscle.

"You remember Cathy, don't you?" Betty prompted when Simon cleared his throat. She waved her hand toward her younger daughter who stood in the center of a group of laughing couples, all in their twenties. "Goodness, I don't know where Patrice could have escaped to. Simon, do you think she and Justin wandered out by the pool?"

Madison congratulated himself that he didn't spill the champagne a waiter had just placed into his hand. The anger that speared through him set his teeth on edge. Whose damn idea of a game was this? Was this some type of competitive showdown between the ex-husband and himself?

He had no intentions of being a party to such a distasteful confrontation. "I think someone has made a mistake here, Mrs. Clayburne. If you'll excuse me."

Simon, in a gesture unseen by Madison, prevented Betty from replying. He stepped in front of Madison as he was turning. "Please accept my apologies. There was a little mix-up in invitations. I assure you there will be no unpleasantries. I would like for you to meet some of our friends."

Quick to see what her position must be, now that both men understood she had manipulated bringing the triangle together, Betty turned on her charm. "Oh, the music has begun again, Mr. Brannen. You will stay for the next selection, at least. This chamber ensemble was playing together when Patrice went to college. I think one of our parties was their very first 'gig,' as they say."

Leaving at this moment proved too awkward. Two women, society queens if he ever saw any, approached the host and hostess. Between gushing remarks on what a lovely party it was and that they should have a meeting to organize the spring flower show, Madison was introduced to both of them. One was the wife of the mayor. The other, a tall, bosomy matriarch who was the president of a local museum, was Adele Fitzsimmons.

"I was just remarking to Mr. Brannen about how lovely the Corelli is this afternoon," Betty explained during a brief lag in the conversation. "Don't you just adore Corelli?"

Madison didn't intend to disagree with his hostess. He had promised himself that this afternoon would flow as smoothly as a stream on a warm day. But the knowledge of Justin's invitation rankled. His correction of Betty's remark rippled off his tongue before he could prevent it.

"Vivaldi, I think," he said. Betty and Adele gaped at him with astonishment, and Simon hid his smile behind his cigarette.

"I beg your pardon, Mr. Brannen," Betty came back with a thin voice.

It was too late to turn back now. Madison cleared his throat and indicated the group of performers beneath the bright canopy outside. "I'm not positive of the opus number," he with intriguing knowledge, "but it's definitely early classical style. Do you hear the contrasting theme?" He paused, listening, then lowered his head. "There. Corelli didn't compose contrasting themes. The *fortspinnung,* as the Germans called it."

"Fortspinnung?" breathed Betty, who had been certain her knowledge was infallible.

Now Madison was forced into the position of explaining. He executed it with such impeccable courtesy, cautious to not make his hostess seem uninformed in any respect, that Simon developed an immediate respect for the younger man.

Madison shrugged in a deprecating way. "It's a fine distinction, Mrs. Clayburne. I wouldn't have known it myself except for a certain music-history teacher who had an exasperating penchant for such things. Corelli, and almost all of the late Baroque composers, used a single theme and simply unfolded it. Or spun it out, so to speak. It resulted in an unbroken flow of musical thought. Quite suitable for my limited mind, you see."

No one could have taken offense at such a tactful correction.

Adele Fitzsimmons adjusted her eyeglasses and gave Madison a second appraisal. "My, my, Mr. Brannen, I do believe you're right. Where *did* you find this young man, Betty?"

Adele was a regular contributor to Justin's newspaper, and Betty went to great lengths to placate her. The smile she gave Adele would have melted iron. Simon withdrew several feet so he could take it all in. He was enjoying himself immensely.

The museum director looped her arm through Madison's. "Now tell me, young man, where did you get your degree?"

Madison laughed. "It wasn't in music, Mrs. Fitzsimmons. The furthest thing from it."

Adele wasn't to be dissuaded. "Tell me, dear boy, what do you think of Jean Philippe Rameau, the celebrated French music theorist and composer?"

Grinning, Madison rubbed his upper lip before he answered. By now, several more of Betty's friends had clustered around. "Ah," he began, "he was an innovator, to say the least. He's probably my hero."

The woman on his arm drew back in curiosity. "Your hero?"

"He did his best work after he was fifty years old."

Adele tipped back her head in a ripple of delighted

laughter. "You come with me," she said and hugged his arm.

Madison's last observation had drawn a round of applause from the ladies and a droll "Right on" from Simon. Betty had never been dense; her quick mind knew a winner when she saw one. She was just about to latch on to Madison herself, meaning to flaunt him before all her guests, when Simon intervened.

"Sorry, Betty," he said, smiling at the ladies and drawing Madison from the center of their circle. "I think it's time Madison had a tour of the grounds."

Madison's gratitude twinkled in his eyes. He threw a look outside at the darkening sky. "We'd better make it quick, sir. I think it's going to rain."

"Impossible," Betty purred from his right elbow.

In a charming, old-world gesture, Madison lifted her hand to his lips and bestowed a kiss on it. "Now it is I who stand corrected," he said and left Betty standing with a queer, unblinking expression on her face.

Patrice saw Madison before he saw her. He strolled across the lawn with her father, moving in his lanky way, smiling as he was introduced to a number of other guests. She thought she would always remember him this way, the breeze ruffling his hair, the graceful way he used his hands, the tilt of his dark head as he listened to the remarks of other people.

She had waited days for this moment. Now that it was upon her she stood trapped with Justin and his friends. She would be thrown into the worst possible predicament, and she thrashed in her mind for some way to escape the manipulation of her ex-husband.

"What's the matter?" Justin demanded as she placed her palms together and held them against her mouth, almost as if she were praying.

Then, because he knew her so well, he glanced around himself, squinting. "Ah yes, I see what the matter is," he murmured softly. "Well, don't get any ideas, little girl."

Defying him, Patrice took several steps away. The breeze caught the shimmery legs of her culottes and molded them until she looked like a gold statuette.

Justin caught up with her. "Would you excuse us, please, John?" he called over his shoulder. "Patrice would like some more champagne."

John was too busy flirting with Vanessa Rheems to care what Patrice wanted. He smiled, then immediately dismissed them.

With growing alarm, Patrice shoved at Justin's cruel fingers as they dug into her arm. "Let me go, Justin. Why don't you go amuse yourself? There must be a dozen women here who would worship at your feet."

Justin only tightened his grip and pulled her close to his hip. Deliberately he walked toward Madison and Patrice's father, certain that Patrice's good breeding wouldn't allow her to draw attention to herself by fighting him now.

"There's only one woman here who I want worshiping at my feet."

"Foot worshiping isn't what I do best," she snapped.

"I don't know what you see in this Madison Brannen, Patrice. Why the man's a commoner. His father was a farmer, for pity's sake!"

Patrice couldn't hold back a laugh. "Oh, Justin, your bigotry is showing. The reason I like Madison Brannen is because he lives by his heart, something you'd never understand because you live by your vanity." She stilled in her tracks. "How do you know what his father was?"

Flicking a piece of lint from his cuff, Justin estimated the remaining distance between Madison and him. "I made it my business to find out."

Patrice's fury hissed between her teeth. "That, Justin, is absolutely despicable!"

Her ex-husband shook his beautiful head from side to side. She wanted to claw her fingernails down the side of his smooth face. Aware of the misleading picture she and Justin would paint for Madison's eye, she wriggled in an attempt to get away.

"Be still, my lovely," he murmured in his Judgment Day voice. "If you don't want to see just how despicable I can really be."

"I couldn't live long enough to see the entire performance."

He laughed maliciously. "Well, I do have my good side, you know. Like the day I went to my bank with your father. Like the day I placed your whole future in my accounts receivable, sweetie. But I'm a generous man."

Justin wasn't joking now, she knew. Justin was a gambler, a shrewd, calculating man who played for very high stakes at times. Something cold tripped up her spine. She ceased resisting him.

"What're you talking about, Justin?"

Knowing full well that Madison would receive the impression that they were engaging in intimate talk, he gazed down at her. He affected a smile.

"How do you think Simon raised the money for this casino he's just opened, baby?"

Giving that menacing announcement time to reap its fullest harvest, he continued. "One flick of my pen would call in the loan. One telephone call could change your whole life. By your life, I mean that of your mother and father, your sister—everyone. Ready to part with that Ferrari, baby? Hmm?"

She could hardly breathe with Justin's fingers digging into her side. The full impact of what he had just told her was still floating somewhere above her. All she fully comprehended was that she was being emotionally blackmailed. In order for her to save her family she must hurt the one man she had ever loved. How? With what strength? With what cold-blooded reflex of survival?

"I've been looking for you, Patrice," her father called across the yards separating them. "Why, hello, Justin. You've met Madison Brannen, I believe."

Far in the distance thunder rumbled. Patrice thought it was perfectly symbolic, commemorating the destruction of her naive, last-ditch effort to find happiness. She suffered the hysterical need to cry. Instead, she smiled.

Justin extended his hand to Madison without blinking an eye.

"Oh, yes. A couple of times. How're you doing, Mr. Brannen? Heard you had a bit of trouble up at Bridgeport. I guess things like that are to be expected these days. Damned shame, though. Much work to rebuild?"

Madison nodded. He shook the younger man's hand. When he spoke, however, his unsmiling eyes were only for Patrice.

"I'm used to hard work," he said absently, growing taut when Patrice looked everywhere except at his face.

Justin could have been discussing sports. "I hear the district attorney may be filing some charges. From what I hear, the investigation is taking forever and the police still aren't sure who planted the bomb. I guess you'd know more about that, wouldn't you, darling?"

With a husbandly intimacy, he drew Patrice so near that his legs connected with the back of hers. His right hand spread upon her waist, across the swell of her abdomen.

All her plans collapsed about her feet like a discarded garment. Justin's was a completely successful display of power. She was so utterly humiliated, so crushed into defeat beyond her wildest nightmares, she nodded. The icy betrayal on Madison's face was the final blow.

Simon knew, instinctively, what was taking place. And his vulnerability was worsened by the fact that he prayed Patrice would find it in her heart to protect him. His eyes met hers, pleading for her discretion.

Madison, however, suffered no diversion except a real need to tear the contemptuous young man apart. All through the war violence had been a part of his life, every hour, every minute of every day. They had all heard the stories of the killing instinct run amuck when men were trained to destroy, then thrust back into society. He had been certain it would never happen to him. Now, reading the challenge hurled at him in this ludicrous manner, he thought he could actually kill a man.

His smile didn't waver. His voice was murderously calm. "Take your hands off her, Harrows," he said.

The whole thing was insane. Patrice wanted to scream that they were all mad!

Simon stretched out a hand meant to comfort her, but she ignored it. She did the only thing she could do. She gestured abstractly.

"Madison, this is a terrible error. Please accept my apologies. I promised Justin I would attend with him, and I—"

"I said, take your hands off her, Justin." Madison's frigid words cut her off as if she had never spoken.

The white of Madison's teeth flashed, entirely out of place with the lacerating whip of his demand. "If you don't, I'm going to break your arm in front of all these people." His tone softened. "Please don't think I won't do it."

The moment of silence was a lifetime, like watching something destroyed and being helpless to move.

"Mr. Brannen." Simon coughed, wishing miserably for his wife. Betty was a master at solving these kinds of problems. "Justin, my boy." He couldn't prevent the quiver in his words. "Look, son—"

"No!" Justin glared at the man who suddenly looked very old. "No, you look, Simon!"

Justin had no time to nail Simon Clayburne to the

wall. Madison absorbed his full attention when he took one step nearer. He wasn't smiling at all now, and the blue of his eyes glittered, steely with the primitive ability to defend what he considered to be his. He began unbuttoning the ruffled cuffs of his shirt-sleeves.

Above them the thunder cracked in a long, grumbling warning of an approaching storm. Patrice began coming unraveled. To her intense horror she hiccuped, then clapped her hands over her mouth. None of the men seemed cognizant of her impending hysteria. They were all too locked in a conflict of wills.

A muscle beside Justin's mouth twitched nervously.

Madison coldly watched the small line of perspiration bead along Justin's upper lip. Without flinching, without lessening his deadly observation of Justin's face, he extended a hand to Patrice.

"Come with me, Patrice," he ordered. "If you'll excuse me, Mr. Clayburne."

Patrice was powerless to obey Madison, regardless of how desperately she wanted to run to him. Her ex-husband was capable of doing everything he threatened.

Justin wiped a hand across his mouth, then moistened his lips. The thunder gave one last warning, and as he glanced upward tiny needles of raindrops began pricking the leaves of the trees, the shrubbery. The splattering was like the ominous ticking of a time bomb.

The suspense played itself out until the last possible moment. Though Justin was a master of intimidation, the care he exerted to preserve his reputation slowly undid him. With finesse, playing his role to the bitter end, he bent his ex-wife's cheek, as if he were handing her over with his blessing.

"Hi, Charlie!" he called over Simon's shoulder to one of his friends who neared them with rapid strides. "We'd better run for shelter, don't you think?"

The flash of lightning that streaked across the sky

startled everyone. Ladies cried out to one another. Grace and elegance were forgotten as guests hurried for the protection of the canopy. The storm swept toward them in furious gray sheets.

As Patrice stood dumbfounded, unable to move even though drops of rain stung her cheeks, Madison grabbed her hand. He began striding swiftly toward the pool house, and she didn't even feel her own feet moving as she went with him. It occurred to her, as Madison half dragged her to the building on the edge of the property, everyone present would soon realize where they had gone. But such reasoning seemed inconsequential in the face of his dark wrath.

Madison had difficulty in opening the stubborn door, but when he leaned his weight against it, it crashed back against the wall. He pushed her in before him and slammed the door shut with a vengeance.

"I don't know—" she began in a shrill cracked voice.

"Oh, I think you do, darling," he growled angrily. "I think you know very well."

Chapter Ten

The rain beating on the roof of the dark pool house was like a drum roll heralding some long-dreaded climax. Patrice's distress was so total that all she could truly grasp was the staccato turbulence of it. That, and the lavish warmth of the luxury that enclosed them.

Motionless, unable to think clearly, she stood in the center of the room with her back to Madison. He hadn't moved from his stance in front of the door. The shadows of chaise lounges and sofas and pillows offered no hospitality. Madison didn't turn on the lights, and she didn't suggest it.

"I'll be damned, Patrice," he said at last. "I'll just be damned."

He wanted an explanation from her, she knew, and she had none to give him. What were her choices? By being in this place with him she could be jeopardizing her entire family. Would she choose between her father or her lover?

"Well," he snapped, "can't you tell me anything? Lie

to me, sweetheart. Tell me it was all some crazy mistake, that I wasn't invited here for one purpose, to be made a fool?"

Her eyes, when she spun about, were so bright with tears they seemed to fill her face. "No, never that!" she cried. "Please, Madison . . ."

How could she ask him to understand?

With one supple movement he loomed over her, towering with his superior power, his magnificent outrage. A strangling sound ripped from his throat. "Please? You ask me *please*? Please, what?"

Distraught, Madison grasped her shoulders. He gave her a none-too-gentle shake and her head fell forward. Like a tiny princess puppet in gold lamé whose strings suddenly ceased to hold it up, she went limp in his arms.

"It wasn't what you think," she mumbled from beneath the tumbling locks of her hair. "Not—"

His wrath wavered. For that moment he seemed almost as vulnerable as she. His arms ceased their punishment and wrapped around her. He drew her to his chest until her heartbeat pulsed into the center of his own senses.

"What am I to do with you?" he muttered. "What am I to do? Everything's so complicated all the time."

Yes, she thought, and stupid. Life was backward, because the person one wanted least to hurt was the one who always got hurt. To love was to hurt! Insanity!

Her whisper was laced with misgiving. "Couldn't you just trust me?"

Madison attempted to clear the hoarseness from his own throat.

"Ah, little one, I'm just a man. A very weak man. A dreamer of dreams. After I saw you that day at Bridgeport I cherished my fantasies like a lovesick kid. I could see myself kissing you . . . everywhere. I was around you, inside you. And it nearly broke me in two,

I wanted you so badly. Then, to come here and find him holding you like he was—"

Abruptly he released her. As if he were unspeakably weary, he moved to a chaise lounge and folded himself down onto the foot of it. His head dropped forward into his hands. Patrice stood observing the defeated posture of him, the way his elbows were braced upon the poor, scarred knees.

Stepping beside his bent head, she combed her fingers through the damp locks of hair and fluffed them into order. She sensed him loosen the tie from around his throat and pry loose the button at his collar. Yet he didn't lift his head to look at her.

"Nothing's changed between Justin and me, Madison. My feelings for you are the same as they were the day you made me admit I loved you. I know it's hard when a person's been married before. I know you have questions. It's only natural to wonder what Justin and I did together, what my feelings were, how much of them are left."

He was listening intently. Even his breathing had stopped.

"There was no feeling to lose when I divorced Justin. I never loved him, Madison. Not in the beginning, not ever."

She wasn't certain if he believed her, for he didn't move a muscle or make a sound of acknowledgment. Her fingers traveled across his shoulders, felt the tenseness there. Then, like a compassionate parent, she drew his head to rest against her waist.

"Why do you let him do things like that to you?" he said.

He was questioning her charade on the lawn, and she shook her head. She could not tell him the truth. Her fingers toyed with the hair furling upon his collar.

"I'm doing the best I can. I swear to you."

Madison turned his face into her waist. He took a

deep breath as if he had come a long way to be at this place. "I've imagined myself going to sleep with my head here," he whispered.

"Have you?" A silvery tremor shot up her legs.

Feeling her tremble, he moved his hands up the backs of her legs, pausing at the swell of her hips, filling them.

"There wasn't any gown around you, either." When his hands crept more intimately, he paused, discovering the impeding fabric of the culottes. "Damnation, Patrice!"

She tried, rather unsuccessfully, to prevent his hands from searching any further. "We have to go back. Don't do that."

"But it's storming," he muttered and pushed her hands aside. His journey to her waist for the closure of her skirt took only a second. "We can't go out," he reminded her with perfect logic, "and they can't come in."

"Patrice?" a voice called over the intercom panel mounted into the wall beside the glass doors. "Are you all right?"

Patrice flinched at the sound of her father's voice as if she and Madison were trapped in a glass bowl for all the Clayburne guests to view. The lift of her regal brows told Madison he had been proved wrong.

"They most assuredly can come in. Yes, Daddy," she pressed down a lever. "We're fine, but I think we may as well wait for the rain to slacken before we walk over."

Her father didn't bring up the subject of Justin, so Patrice didn't either, though she pictured her ex-husband standing before the French doors of the east room, brooding. He would, undoubtedly, imagine the very worst of her. What would that vengeance cost Simon Clayburne?

Madison, who had ambled up behind Patrice as she talked to Simon, unhooked the band of her skirt.

Grabbing at it, trying to reply to her father in a normal voice, Patrice ended up sounding breathless. She slapped at Madison's hand as he tugged the culottes low on her hips like a belly dancer's costume.

"We'll be over in a little while, Daddy," she promised brokenly. "We have soft drinks and things in the refrigerator."

Apparently Simon didn't deduce the halfhearted scuffle that was being waged as they talked. He broke the connection at his end, and Patrice whirled on Madison, flushed and scolding.

"You have no idea of the position you're putting me in!" she cried against the turmoil of the rain.

Lifting up the cumbersome hem of her half-removed culottes, she darted around him. Her hands shook as she rehooked the waist. She tossed back her head to repair some of the disorder of her hair.

"Everyone knows where we are. You know what they'll speculate about."

"By everyone, you mean him, don't you?" Madison ceased teasing her. He leaned back against the wall, and his eyes narrowed as they roamed over her disarray. "The mighty Justin Harrows will speculate about what we're doing?"

"That's not fair!" she blurted. "I explained to you—"

"I don't like the man's hands on you, Patrice!"

"Neither do I!"

"Well, make it clear to him."

Her head bent. "You don't know what you're talking about."

"Then explain it to me," he demanded with quiet authority.

Patrice stood rubbing her temples as they throbbed mercilessly. She heaved a discouraged sigh. "I can't."

Madison heaved himself away from the wall and strode to the cabinet of a bar off the main pavilion. Bending, he searched through its contents until he

211

found a decanter to his pleasing and poured himself a liberal drink.

Patrice watched him toss it down and bare his teeth at its sting. "You just don't understand," she pleaded with him. "If you—"

He said nothing when she stopped talking in midsentence. He merely poured himself another drink, lifted it as if in salute to her refusal, sent it scalding down with the other, and slammed his glass to the counter.

For a moment Patrice stood chewing at her upper lip. Seeing that he was intent upon washing her away with her father's Scotch, she became furious. "There's no reasoning with you!" she accused.

She walked swiftly to one of the dressing rooms in a wing near the pool. She positioned herself before the mirror and braced her hands upon the edge of a dresser to stop her trembling. Justin was ruining her life again. For so long she had thought she didn't want Madison. But now she did, and Justin stood between them like a living wall.

On the verge of screaming at the unfairness, she searched through the drawers until she found a hairbrush. She was winding up the long swath of hair, her hands lifted to the crown of her head, when Madison filled the doorway of the tiny enclosure.

His reflection fit into the mirror behind hers—his opened suit coat, his loosened tie, his unbuttoned shirt. She met the dark burning blue of his gaze with slackened lips. He stood so near that his breath warmed the side of her jaw. As the musky scent of his cologne mingled with the smell of fine liquor she flicked her tongue over her mouth and swallowed.

Without an apology, without saying he understood, Madison's hands closed over both her uplifted ones. In catastrophic slow motion he lifted first one hand, then the other. The shimmering length of her hair cascaded between them like a cloud. It caught on his shoulders, on the buttons of his shirt.

Patrice couldn't move. She was a spellbound dove in the path of a veteran predator who meant to have it all. She didn't even drop her hands. They remained lifted, hovering at the tendrils that swirled about her ears as she listened to the raggedness of her own breathing.

Madison held her unwavering gaze in the reflection as he negotiated the top button of her blouse, then the next and the next. The blouse floated to the floor in flickering disregard. Her bra was a lacy film, worse than nothing. As he stared at it his breathing quickened noticeably, yet his fingers never hesitated in their purpose. The hooks at her skirt yielded. With them loosed, he removed his hands and let the garment slither, of its own accord, into a pool of gold about her feet.

"Oh, Madison," she whimpered, hardly recognizing her own voice. A pink stain highlighted her cheeks and slowly spread its flush downward over her throat. Her knees threatened to collapse beneath her.

Not replying, Madison reached around her. His hands met at her middle. He pressed against her hips, his desire raging, undeniable, compelling.

It was useless to resist. The fire that radiated up through her own limbs was, in its way, as urgent as that which thrust him so boldly against her.

He freed the clasp on her bra with a whispering click, and Patrice began trembling at the sight of her own nakedness. In the soft light her breasts were very white and tipped with a tint of the palest rose. They longed for his touch, but he didn't caress them. He slipped the index finger of each hand beneath the gauzy waist of her panty hose. With a flex of his knees he stripped them off her as neatly as a forester splitting a timber with one fell stroke.

Crossing her arms over her bosom, her shyness as charming as her pale beauty, she turned. She expected him to crush her hard against him, to kiss her. But he buried one knee into the carpet and wrapped his arms about her knees. His fingers buried into the soft cushion of her hips with the same aggression as his lips, which began exploring the silk of her belly. Lower his mouth wandered, and lower still, until she slowly shaped her hands about his head. She heard her own breath as it gasped, held, then yielded with a single, surrendering sigh.

"I said no to you once," he mumbled as he found the final sublimity of all her sensations, which would bind her to him. "Never again."

Readying themselves to return to the house and face the Clayburne guests with equanimity wasn't easily accomplished. Physical appeasement had only served to make Patrice delightfully uninhibited.

"I should fatten you up a bit, my man," she teased. She was clad in the wisp of her bikini panties and was torturing him with her leisure in putting on her bra.

"What's wrong with me? I'm perfect." He laughed, then pretended to scowl. "Don't you like my flat stomach?"

Giggling, she fastened the clip of her underwear and leaned over to tweak one of the sooty curls that traced a slender line below his waist. "I love it. But I can see your ribs. Look."

She walked her fingers up the lean torso as Madison endeavored to zip up his trousers. He winced at the tickling sensation and playfully slapped at her hand. Then Patrice, glowing with newfound energy, tormented him in earnest. Madison, no more eager to be tickled than any other man, planted a lusty whack across her bottom.

The tussle ended on the floor with Madison straddling her waist, pinning both arms out from her side, devouring the sight of her breasts bursting from the inadequate little garment.

"You win!" she choked and covered his shoulders

with adoring kisses when he drew himself upon her, bracing his weight upon his arms.

"You make it hard—"

"I know." She laughed.

He smothered her with a noisy series of kisses. "Devil-tongued woman." He glared at her. "You make it hard to leave you. I don't want to go back."

Patrice stopped laughing. The thoughts of leaving him were painful already, and they hadn't even parted. Before, when they had both been burning with the urgency of satisfying each other, he had whispered guttural words of love. She had believed them. Now, when he said he didn't want to leave her, she waited for the inevitable proposal of marriage. She would not deny him this time. She would say yes with all her heart.

But Madison asked nothing. Vaguely disappointed, she knew it was her fault. She had denied him once too often. If marriage was discussed between them again, she would have to bring it up.

So she watched him dress with subdued fascination. She loved his grace when he stooped for his shoes, and the suppleness of his hands as he laced them. She dressed herself with a nagging prick of anger that their love could not go on forever.

Madison swore a hearty oath and ripped the aggravating tie from about his neck. Patrice, dressed now, was in the process of arranging her hair. She smiled at his bluster.

"Love does nothing to sweeten your temper, I see," she chided and plucked the offending twill from his fingers. "I'm an expert at this."

Realizing her error of referring to Justin, her lightness dwindled. For a moment they stood measuring the tension. Madison broke it.

"Look, Patrice, you can't keep guarding every word about Justin. I know he's been a part of your past. I can handle it. Honestly. Now, if you can do something with this miserable apparatus—God curse the fool who invented it—do it quickly. It's stopped raining."

She tilted her head and listened for the sound of the rain. Water splattered down the gutters, and only a distant complaint of thunder echoed above them. Grimacing, she pushed up his chin and flicked the tie up and over, tugged it out twice and adjusted the sides of the bow.

"There! Like new."

He grinned, then shot his black brows high. "Hardly."

She laughed. "Restored then, idiot. But what about me?"

"Walk back with your hair down. Everyone knows we got caught in the rain, for heaven's sake. Fix it over there where you can sit down and do it right." He coughed at his unintentional witticism. "Not that you don't already know how to do it, love. You do it right. Say, isn't that a song?"

"If it's not, it ought to be. Look." She stepped to the glass doors and pulled open the drapes. "Mother's opening up the doors. 'Course no one would dare put a foot on the lawn. I think it's a gentle hint to us."

Before Madison could reply, Patrice pushed open the doors and waved as if they had been waiting on pins and needles until the storm ended and they could make their return.

"You're a rather remarkable little hypocrite, my darling," he observed as they gingerly picked their way across the saturated lawn.

Without a moment's deliberation, she said, "I've worked hard at it."

Madison didn't think she was joking when she said it.

Patrice traipsed across the most amazing boundaries of the truth for Betty when she and Madison returned to the guests. She explained the state of her hair with such charm that the subject was promptly dismissed. When she observed how quickly her mother's friends latched on to Madison, she didn't think anyone was too interested in the state of her coiffure.

"I think I'll run upstairs and finish drying my hair, Mother," she said.

Betty stepped beside her older daughter and they both watched Madison. Adele Fitzsimmons had her hand on his shoulder, sharing something of an absolutely delicious nature by the look of her smile. He was listening politely and made some remark Patrice could not hear. Feminine laughter rippled across the room.

Betty tapped her own jaw with a forefinger. "I think your Mr. Brannen has just stolen my party," she told Patrice.

Laughing, Patrice nodded. "Be careful, Mother. He may steal you, too."

"I doubt that," Betty retorted as Patrice slipped unobtrusively toward the hallway.

The upstairs was refreshingly quiet as Patrice reached the landing. One entire wing of the upper floor was occupied by her parents' opulent rooms—an office, a sitting room, two bedrooms, a sewing room, and two baths. She and Cathy had occupied rooms toward the west flank of the property. Betty still kept the rooms just as they were when they were girls with their stuffed animals and posters of popular teen idols.

Feeling oddly happy, she breezed past Cathy's old room. Muffled giggles emanated through the walls. Patrice smiled. Gossiping friends, she thought, who were probably sprawled over the bed and the floor exchanging "he said this" and "she said that" a dozen times.

Even as a girl she had never fit in any of those "girl talk" sessions. But today, still tingling with the wonderful sensation of having been thoroughly loved, she paused before her sister's door. Why not? For once, perhaps it would be fun to make fun of Mrs. Edleberg's hat and the way Evan Sinclair clicked his heels when he talked.

"Cathy?" She pushed open the door with a sheepish smile for interrupting. "D'you mind if I get in on thi—"

The sight of her sister jerking up into a sitting position, her blouse half off, her hair a mess, with Justin slowly dragging himself off of her, wasn't something Patrice could handle with any degree of finesse. She couldn't even back out the door the same way she came in. Like some stupid robot she remained rooted to the floor, her mouth open, her eyes incredulous.

"Oh!" Cathy's whimper was the most pitiful entreaty Patrice thought she had ever heard.

"I'm sorry," Patrice managed to choke out. "I—" She finally recovered enough of her wits to turn around.

"No!" Cathy yelped, knocking aside Justin's muffled attempts to advise her. "No, wait! Please . . . don't go. Patty—"

Justin seemed to be the only one of the three with enough presence of mind to shut the door. With a brazen glare at Patrice, he stormed past her and slammed the door, locking it this time.

"You should have done that earlier," Patrice observed dryly.

Bursting into distraught tears, Cathy threw herself facedown on the bed and buried her face in a pillow. "We didn't do anything," she wept, barely coherent. "I swear we didn't."

"For God's sake, Cathy!" Justin lashed out. "Don't apologize to her! It's none of her business what you do."

He took several steps toward Patrice, but Patrice, for once, stood her ground with him. She didn't budge an inch.

He turned up a palm. "Well, sugar, it's tit for tat, eh? You and Brannen. Cath and me."

A scalding fury darkened Patrice's already burning

face. "Like you say, Justin, it's nobody's business, either way."

He laughed wickedly. "Well, I like to keep things in the family."

Patrice had often wondered if she were capable of violence. Now she knew she was; she wanted to rip Justin apart. Her green eyes turned an emerald color. "Vengeance upon me, Justin?"

"You might say that."

They stood squared off like duelists prepared to fight to the death. The usual smirk curled the edges of Justin's mouth. But Patrice, calling upon all the skills she had developed in **her** training, removed all excesses from her mind. She gave the appearance of being supremely cool, totally lacking emotion.

For a moment Justin considered this new view of his ex-wife. He knew she was very angry, but he wasn't sure just how much.

"Hell," he said and grinned.

"Yes, hell," she repeated. "That's what you're about to find yourself in, Justin. You forget that my sister is a married woman, married to someone not entirely helpless. I wonder what Harold will have to say about all this."

"Patrice!" Cathy cried. She dove off the bed and began putting herself back together again in a frenzy.

"I told you we weren't doing anything!" she wailed as she searched for her shoes. "Good Lord, how did I ever get myself into this?"

"The same way we all get ourselves in messes," her sister replied levelly, her eyes not blinking as they defied Justin. "With Justin it's easy. And you're only a human being. Human beings make mistakes."

Such sympathy colored Patrice's reply, Cathy's tear-stained face lifted.

Patrice shook her head mournfully. "But he's such a bad choice, Cath."

For a moment, as he considered just how much he

had compromised himself for a few stolen kisses, Justin's beauty dulled. He seemed oblivious of Cathy's distress, even of his ex-wife's anger. He turned abruptly, his forefinger curved along the side of his mouth.

"Say, Patrice, what you said about Harold . . ." His words dwindled off as he shrugged. He grinned his cherub's smile. "You wouldn't really . . . say anything."

Patrice smiled mirthlessly. It seemed, at this moment, that she had waited three years to unleash a maelstrom of wrath upon this cruel man. Outwardly serene, however, she stepped before him. Her hands didn't even clinch.

"Justin"—she lifted her face prettily—"it would give me great pleasure. And when Harold is finished suing his wife for divorce, naming you corespondent, I think I'll have a little talk with Judge Masters. He might have a few doubts about your executorship of the Harrows Trust. Of course, I realize I might not be able to do any real damage there, but I think I can promise you that your credibility will never be the same."

"But—"

She drew up to her full height. Control was in her hands, and she wielded it majestically. "Don't ever threaten me again as you did this afternoon, Justin. What you and my father do is your own business. Leave me out of it. Do you understand that?"

With an embarrassment he was constrained to hide, Justin jammed both fists deep into his pockets. He tried to smile, but a muscle beside his mouth spasmed. He quickly removed a hand to wipe across it.

"Well, well, well," he said brokenly, then cleared his throat. "So the perfect little Patrice has found her tongue at last. You know, that's what we all called you in college—Prim Patty Primrose. One of the guys bet me his crib notes I couldn't seduce you."

Patrice was not about to relinquish one iota of the victory that hovered so closely. She forced her tone to sound ridiculously sweet. "Life is full of little problems, isn't it?"

Behind them Cathy sat slumped onto the bed, speechless.

Justin suffered difficulty in maintaining his facade. He moved near the door. With his hand on the knob, he looked back. "Maybe I did come on a little strong out there with Brannen today."

Flinching, tightening her fists until her nails cut into her palms, Patrice said nothing.

The glitter in Justin's eyes heightened, almost as if he were anxious that she understand. "I've known men like Brannen before. They come back from the war and flaunt their heroism and smile their do-good smiles like they're nothing but sweetness and light. Men like him make me want to—"

"Madison is ten of you, Justin Harrows!" Patrice lashed at him. She could bear his abuse of her, but she would not allow him to condemn the man she loved.

"Why don't you get out of this house?" she cried, flinging out her hand. "Leave the Clayburne family alone. Attach yourself to someone else. Bleed them for a while."

Finally breaking through her icy control, he wagged a finger beneath her nose. Behind the leering grin, however, Patrice read his defeat. Justin had been successfully forced into a stalemate. The one thing she had learned in twenty-five years was to leave a person enough dignity to make a retreat. So she swallowed down the bitter dregs of her temper and made her face bland.

As if he expected her to say something more, he waited. When she didn't, he touched his forehead in a mock salute. "I guess I'll be toddling along, ladies," he joked. The muscle in his cheeks twitched again.

She wanted to remind him that his tail was tucked between his legs. Instead she smiled coldly. "I think we know what we expect of the other."

Though Justin would not satisfy her by agreeing, Patrice knew that she had won. The door shut quietly behind him, and for a moment all the two women did was remain perfectly still and listen to the sound of their own dejected thoughts.

The sob from Cathy broke the spell. Feeling enormous compassion, Patrice sat beside her on the bed. She drew her younger sister's head to her shoulder.

"Don't waste your grief on him, Cathy," she consoled. "This will all go away. You have two little girls who adore you and a husband who cares what happens to you. It could be a lot worse."

"Should I tell Harold?" came the strangled question. "About this?"

Considering a moment, Patrice spoke honestly. "Do you think it will help Harold to know? Will it make your marriage better?"

Cathy considered for a moment, then shook her head. "But I need to get it off my chest."

"At his expense?"

With a wadded tissue Cathy blotted her eyes. "It would be selfish, wouldn't it?"

"That's the price we pay for doing wrong, Cath. We bear our guilts alone. It's harder, yes, but at least only one person is hurt."

Keeping her eyes downcast, flicking at her thumbnail, Cathy licked her lips. "Patrice, it's not fair the way Mother treats you."

"No, Cathy, please don't—"

Cathy lifted her head. "I want to say it. For a long time I've known that Mother is partial to me. She can't see a single flaw in me, and I swear I've never done anything to encourage that. If I were worth a copper penny I'd go to Mother right now and tell her what a mistake she's made."

All during Cathy's explanation, Patrice sat shaking her head. When the silence hung between them, Patrice let out her breath. Now her own eyes were a misty sea-green.

"I used to be bitter about that," she confessed slowly. "But that doesn't matter now. Mother will have to trust me because she wants to, Cathy. Not because of what you say, or what anyone says." She paused. "It doesn't really matter anymore. Someone loves me. Deeply. It's enough. Now! I think we ought to repair some of this mess and get back downstairs."

A wordless smile passed between the two women. They were growing up. They weren't asking for absolutes any longer. They were accepting the weaknesses in themselves and in their parents. It felt very, very good.

"I think you're right," Cathy agreed, dragging herself off the bed. "I want to go home, do you know that?"

Patrice smiled. "I think it'll be better between you and Harold from now on."

Cathy's life was not the only thing that had received a fresh beginning, Patrice thought as she brushed her hair. She had a new insight into her own strengths. No longer did Justin have the ability to hurt her. This had been true for some time, but only since she had begun loving Madison had she truly realized it.

There was no need to tell her father what had happened here today. It would only expose Cathy and would embarrass him for being so weak concerning Justin. Most of all, she didn't want Madison to suffer the anger of learning how Justin had used them all. It was over. It was now past history.

So, in the way of a wise woman, she tucked this last triumph far back in her mind. She deserved no medals for growing up. She only hoped it hadn't come too late to take what happiness she could with Madison. He deserved so much more than what he had gotten.

"What took you so long, pretty lady?" Madison murmured over the crown of her head as they returned to the guests after he had met her coming down the stairs. "I was about to come up there and start opening doors."

The skies had cleared, but the musicians were packing up, and people were making the amenities of departure. It had been a strange day—a horrible, wonderful, disillusioning one. Patrice took Madison's arm and ignored her mother's curiosity.

"I had a little matter with Justin that needed tidying up." She smiled up at him. "It was nothing."

His mouth curved into a smile that brimmed with love for her. "Well, aren't you going to tell me?"

Lowering her eyes, because she didn't want him to see the price she had paid for growing up, she touched the center button on his shirt. "Someday," she said breathlessly. "Maybe when I'm old and gray and sit in my rocking chair by the fire."

"I will love you more then than I do now."

The second was a sterling one. Patrice knew she would look back upon this moment as the true beginning of her life. She had no more doubts about her feelings. They would go with her to the end of her days.

There, in her mother's house, before anyone who cared enough to turn and see, she hugged Madison with perfect trust. It was her way of telling them all she was proud to be loved by him.

Madison understood.

Chapter Eleven

$\mathcal{L}$oving and being loved lent Patrice's days a vibrant sparkle she had never experienced before. For the first time in her life the minutes and hours of her life had a center: Madison Brannen. During the times he was out of the city her whole existence was focused on the telephone beside her bed.

Alexander Graham Bell's invention, she discovered, was a vastly erotic implement when one was in love. Late at night she murmured things into the receiver she would never have had the courage to tell Madison face-to-face. He loved her wicked suggestions and the provocative sensuality of her moods. She had visited Paul Nelson at his office for some birth-control pills, she told him. Paul had looked at her with provoked curiosity but had said nothing.

"Maybe he thinks you're getting promiscuous," Madison teased. "Maybe he wishes he were the man in your life. Keep him in suspense."

She laughed. "Oh, he knows who it is, all right. But Paul has always thought I was too much like my mother to risk getting hooked up with a rogue like you." Translated, that meant, *I could become permanently hooked up with you if you would only say the word.*

But Madison only chuckled from his end of the line as he lay sprawled on a hotel divan in Cincinnati, Ohio, where he was finishing some work for the city. One long leg was thrown over its back.

"Darling, no one could be less like your mother. How's the queen of Atlantic City doing, by the way?"

These days Betty was grudgingly tolerating the fact that Patrice and Madison were an item.

"She hasn't given up, though," Patrice admitted. "I think she still believes that someway, somehow, Justin and I will get back together."

"It's a good thing I'm coming home in two days," he told her affectionately.

He couldn't get home too soon, Patrice mused as she dressed for work the next day. The telephone was only a poor substitute for a man. She was starving for the sight of him.

On her way out the front door, the telephone jangled. A bit impatiently she answered it.

"Yes," responded a strange voice, which was woven into a tapestry of many other voices and a loudspeaker booming in the background. "You may find this a strange question, but are you the Miss Harrows who is a friend of someone named . . ." A pause, then, "Someone named Madison Brannen?"

Work ceased to matter. She frowned darkly. "Who is this?"

"This is the bus station. My name is Stella Proveski in Personnel. I have a little boy here who says his name is Miles Hathaway. He's trying to find his uncle, he says."

A sensation of delayed reaction drifted down Patrice's legs. She groped behind herself for a chair.

Though she couldn't remember Rose's married name, this had to be Miles.

"Could I speak to him, please?"

"Of course. He's pretty frightened right now. Hold on."

Considering the bombshell just dropped into her lap, Patrice was none too calm, herself. "Hello? Is that you, Miles?"

The boyish voice cracked like fragile, aging tissue. "Are you Madison's friend? The lady who came to visit us at my grandma's house?"

The helpless plea turned Patrice into an immediate rock of strength.

He interrupted before she could answer. "You remember," he desperately prompted, "the raft? You said you knew how to build a raft?"

"Yes, of course I remember, darling. Does your grandma know where you are?"

Silence. Then, "N-no."

Patrice had guessed as much. "Look, Miles. You stay exactly where you are with that nice lady. There's nothing to be afraid of now. I'll drive down to the bus station in a flash and pick you up. Then we can come to my house and decide what to do."

He breathed heavily into the receiver, as if his childish judgment were sifting through her words. "You're . . . you're sure you won't forget to come get me?"

What had Rose done to this child? Patrice slumped in disbelief. What had possessed him to run away? And how had he ever managed to find his way to Atlantic City without someone getting curious enough to locate Virginia Brannen? Miles, undoubtedly, had been extremely clever.

Patrice calmed her voice. "Miles, I promise you, cross my heart, that I'll be there in a few minutes. Hang up the phone now, sweetheart. I'm ready to leave this very minute."

Once Patrice arrived at the bus terminal, she rushed straight to the ticket desk as the woman in charge of Personnel had directed her. One look at the pale, frightened face of Miles as he stood beside a worried woman undid Patrice completely. Bending, she threw open her arms. The little boy hurtled himself into them.

He sobbed out his nightmare upon her shoulder. "I ran out of money," he wept. "The man on the bus bought me a hamburger. I told lots and lots of lies. Mamaw says its terrible to tell lies."

"Shh." Patrice smoothed his tousled head and rocked him in her arms. "It's all right. You're okay now. No one is going to make you do anything you don't want to." Leaning back from him she blotted his tears with her fingers. "Dry your face. I'm starving to death, and you're just the gentleman I'd most like to have breakfast with. What do you say?"

The crying dwindled to an occasional sniffle. "Where's Madison?"

Brushing his hair out of his eyes, Patrice smiled. "He's out of town right now. But we'll talk to him, and then we'll meet his plane. He'll come home the minute he learns you've come to visit."

Over the head of the boy, Patrice grimly handed Stella Proveski a twenty-dollar bill. Stella shook her head.

"Please," urged Patrice. "As a personal favor to me for your trouble and your kindness. And thank you very, very much."

"You're welcome. And you, little man," the woman cajoled, "had better get some food in your stomach. Your jeans are about to fall off."

Miles blinked through tear-studded eyelashes. "My uncle's going to buy me a cowboy belt," he assured her gravely.

Stella ruffled his hair. "And I think you're going to be just fine with this nice lady."

The message that the two women tacitly exchanged

was mutual; Miles Hathaway had suffered a trauma so painful to him he probably would never tell anyone the entirety of it.

At the door of the bus station Miles rotated toward Stella. Watching them leave, she waved. Before he followed Patrice out onto the busy street, Miles shyly waved back.

When Madison learned what Miles had done he was livid. A stream of hostilities against Rose rushed past his lips, and he cut them off with only the strongest self-discipline.

"I'm leaving immediately," he clipped. "Meet me at the airport."

Patrice tried to allay his worries. "Please don't worry yourself into a state, Madison. Miles and I are doing fine. I do think you should call your mother and let her know he's all right. I started to do it myself, but you really should."

He agreed, but he asked if she would take Miles on a quick shopping trip and buy everything he would need for a few days.

"You know I will." She smiled to herself; she knew the first thing she would buy was a cowboy belt. "What will I tell him?"

"Tell him he and I are going to spend a few days fishing. I've got to repair whatever made him run away like this."

An unexpected feeling of being excluded washed over Patrice like a spray of icy water. She didn't know which was worse—being left out or her resentment of it. She was above this selfish reaction! she berated herself. Madison's devotion to Miles was one of the things she loved about him. No one in her right mind was jealous of a child!

Still, Madison's concern when he handed her his attaché case at the airport and lifted Miles up in his arms was painful. To stand patiently by and watch the two of them with their heads touching tapped a source of maturity she had never realized she possessed before.

Love meant sharing, she reminded herself. Love was giving more than one had to give. It was an emptying of oneself for another person, no matter what form it took.

When Madison took her in his arms she clung tightly.. She truly didn't mean to cry, but when he stood holding her for long moments, not kissing her, not moving, she whispered, "I have never loved you as much as now," hot tears filling her eyes.

He drew back and peered deep into her soul. "What did I ever do to deserve your love?"

Holding his face between her hands, she adored the web of fatigue about his eyes, the pinched corners of his mouth, the grief lurking just below the surface.

"You once sat in an ambulance beside a woman and helped her without asking questions. I feel grateful to be able to do the same for you. I love you."

Without speaking, as people passed them on both sides and Miles waited wonderingly beside him Madison drowned in her brimming gaze. He kissed her with more tenderness than she had ever known.

Madison and Miles had only been gone two hours when Patrice walked wearily into her living room. All the phone calls had been made, all the explanations given to Virgina. Now, all that was left was her loneliness until the two of them returned.

The hour was still early, half-past eight o'clock. Feeling as if her poor body had been shoved through a giant wringer, Patrice dropped onto the divan and lay back, covering her eyes with her arm. When the doorbell chimed, she was so nearly asleep she jumped up with a start.

She hurried to the door, swept it open, and stared straight into the eyes of Rose.

"Rose!" she breathed in disbelief.

"I'm sorry to come in without callin' or anything, Miss Harrows," Madison's sister apologized.

Refraining from blurting a dozen questions that demanded immediate answers, Patrice swept back her arm. "Please, come in. I guess you've spoken with your mother. Madison called her earlier."

"Yeah. She told me where Miles had come. Lord-amercy, that boy has driven me clear out of my skull, doin' this. I can't imagine what got into him."

Patrice could imagine quite easily what had gotten into Miles, but she offered no advice, no criticism. Instead she invited Rose into the kitchen and gestured toward a chair as she put water on to boil.

"I hate to tell you this," Patrice began hesitantly as she spooned tea into a new teapot, "but Miles isn't here just now."

Rose's chair scraped on the floor. "What?"

Patrice waved her down with her spoon. "Now, now, he's fine. Madison drove him to a quiet little camping spot not too far from here. He wanted to calm him down and make sure that nothing like this ever happened again. He had no idea you would be coming."

When the tea was placed before her, Rose sat staring at it as if she could see the future somewhere in the amber liquid. Absently she picked up her spoon and stirred.

"Well, I guess I have that one coming. And it's all right. I get so damned mad at Madison sometimes."

"You don't have to expla—"

"That was really the lowest, what he did, you know. Telling the judge that I couldn't take care of my own son."

This entire line of conversation was nothing that Patrice hadn't heard before. But she had never been an integral part of it before, either. She wished Rose wouldn't confide in her, but she poured her own tea and sat across from the younger woman, listening quietly.

"If he'd just been nicer about it, I would have let him keep Miles for a while. Honest." Rose looked up and blinked. With the fingertips of one hand she wiped away mascara smudges from below her eyes.

Patrice said nothing in reply.

Hesitating, Rose lifted the cup to her lips. She was dressed in jeans and a plaid shirt, topped with a denim jacket with pockets and epaulets. She lowered the teacup, brushed one shoulder, then drummed her fingernails on the surface of the table.

"Coming up here I was thinking," she began.

Patrice held her breath. "And?"

Rose's head dropped forward onto the heel of her hand. "Oh, God, Miss Harrows, my life is such a mess right now. I don't hardly know how to put it back together."

Patrice prudently guarded her words. "You're talking about Bert?"

Nodding, Rose fished in her pocket for a tissue. "He really cares about me, you know. I'm not making that up, either. He's the first man I ever met who didn't want to jump in the sack, then say 'see ya around.' "

"You're too fine a woman to let someone use you, Rose." Patrice attempted to encourage her for Madison's sake. "Miles is such a lovely little boy. You two could be a real family."

Rose's eyes snapped. "Yeah, that's easy for you to say. You've got a profession, and I just finished high school by the skin of my teeth. What's for me if I don't marry some man?"

"A lot, Rose! A damn good deal more than you're reaching out for!" Horrified at herself, Patrice leaned back in her chair with a heavy sigh. "I'm sorry. I had no right to say that."

"Aw, that's all right. I know what you're talking about. Look, I really think I have a chance with Bert, you know? He says he wants to marry me. But he doesn't want no kids. Not now."

Nervous, Rose got up from the table and began walking about the room. She flicked at a glossy leaf of the plant trailing over the countertop. "I don't know what to do. I think I'd really be able to start over with Bert."

The allusion hung suspended between them, teetering precariously until Patrice decided to come straight to the point.

"Do you have an idea?" she asked.

The prompting was all Rose needed. She had, evidently, thought this over for some time. Perhaps she had discussed it with Bert.

"I wouldn't mind if Madison kept Miles for a while. Just until I got things all worked out. I might've suggested it before if he hadn't acted like such a beast."

"Rose, I know for a fact that Madison highly regrets what he did. He loves the boy dreadfully. He was worried, that's all. In spite of what you feel right now, Madison loves you. He only wants the best for you and Miles, believe me."

Slumping back against the counter Rose toyed with a strand of her hair.

"D'you suppose Miles could stay here?" She shrugged. "Just for a while until I get things all worked out? You wouldn't be out any. I'm sure Madison would pay for everything."

"It's not the money, for pity's sake! Rose, that's asking a lot of Madison—giving him the boy then taking him away."

Rose's small fist crashed down with a thump. "Well, that's the best I can do. Look, Bert's waiting for me in the car—"

Rising to her feet, Patrice was surprised. "Why didn't you say something? Invite him in."

"No, no. We really have to be going. I just wanted to make sure Miles was all right and see if he . . . well, if he could—"

What was the use in prolonging it? thought Patrice.

233

She loved Madison; she knew his mind. So, she spoke for him. "Of course. Leave him here. He'll be all right. And we'll keep in touch with Virginia. Madison will call her the minute he gets home, I'm sure."

That seemed to be all the reassurance Rose needed. Rising hastily, she moved toward the door. She was quite uncomfortable now.

At a loss, hoping she had done the right thing, Patrice ambled behind her toward the front door. When they stood awkwardly in front of it, Rose turned around.

"Hey, I really hate to ask this, seein' as how you've been so nice and and all. But I . . ."

After a pause, Patrice urged her. "You what?"

"I really could use a couple of dollars if you can spare 'em. I spent the last cent I had getting up here. Just some gas money, you understand."

Patrice thought she understood quite clearly. She went immediately for her purse.

"Will fifty dollars be enough?" she asked, removing some bills and folding them.

A smile wreathed Rose's face. She opened her arms and hugged Patrice's neck. Patrice was amazed at how hard her slender body was, like a boy's. The display, considering the circumstances, unnerved her. She forced a smile and patted Rose's back.

"You really have a lot going for you, Rose. Try hard to be your own person. You can make it on your own, I know you can."

"Sure." Rose smiled and nodded as she curled her fingers about the doorknob.

Beneath a streetlight a number of blocks away, Bert Stevenson was parked in his battered green Mustang. As Rose climbed wearily into the car and dropped back against the seat with a groan he started the engine. He turned on the parking lights and watched her craftily.

Only the dashboard light threw a hazy glow into the interior of the car.

"Well, did you do any good?" he asked edgily.

Rose smoothed back her hair and watched him light a cigarette. After he had taken a drag she extended her hand. Bert placed the white cylinder between her fingers and let his hand drop heavily to her thigh.

Smoke swirled upward as Rose dug her fingers into her pants pocket. Withdrawing the two twenty-dollar bills and the ten, she thrust them at Bert. Without hesitating he took them, folded them and slipped them into his shirt pocket. Grinning, he buttoned the pocket.

He turned, and in the same motion began undoing the buttons to Rose's plaid shirt. His hands were not gentle when he slipped them inside.

Gritting her teeth, Rose forced a smile on her lips. When she found herself shoved back hard against the seat she didn't fight his assault. She didn't fight anyone's assault anymore. She only steeled herself to the demands of this man's hands and hoped that he wouldn't leave her.

Patrice, when the door closed, leaned back against it and marveled at the complexity of the sadness she suffered. Inadvertently, Rose had changed the course of her entire future with Madison.

Oh, she knew what she should do, what she must do. But was it what she wanted to do? Madison had, in the final analysis, gotten what he wanted. He could raise Miles as the boy should be raised since Rose would not come back, not for a long time, if ever. Now Madison had the one thing capable of filling the empty hole in his life.

Where did that leave her? She wasn't even certain he wanted to marry her anymore. Perhaps she shouldn't be so honest, so honorable. Perhaps she should be a bit more clever. With a tiny bit of feminine guile she could win another proposal of marriage from him. She could rebuild her own bridges with Madison and then tell him the truth.

With a pain gripping the inside of her lungs, strangling the breath from her, she rushed to her bedroom. She began throwing things into a suitcase. She wasn't precisely sure where Madison and Miles were camped. Yet one thing was certain; even if it cost her a possible marriage and a future, she could not deceive the man she loved.

Chapter Twelve

$\int$tay tuned for the six o'clock evening news following this announcement," a faceless, round-voweled voice invited from the speaker of the car radio.

Flicking off the dial, Patrice wriggled uncomfortably in the leather seat. Since noon she'd been driving around Lake Lenape, weaving futilely around every logical campsite north of Mays Landing. Madison and Miles could be anywhere. The lake was bordered with hundreds of suitable hideaways. She was tired and hungry and discouraged and needed to go to the bathroom.

Spotting the blinking sign of a bait and tackle shop nestled in a nearby cove, she swerved the Ferrari off the road. Dust whirled past as she braked. This area could use some rain, she thought as she crawled out of the car and bent backward to pop the kinks from her spine.

"What can I do for you?" a cheery old gentleman called from behind an antiquated cash register.

Peering through a smudged canister, she selected a

package of crackers. She smiled doubtfully. "Not much unless you can work miracles."

She snapped the cap off a soft-drink bottle and described her virtually hopeless plight of trying to locate one lone man and a young boy. She was about to decide she had run into her dozenth dead end when she offhandedly mentioned Madison's antique pickup. The man's wizened face crinkled with interest.

"Oh yeah, I remember him comin' in here with that truck. Sure did bring back a heap of mem'ries, it did. I used to have one just like it before the war. That was the Big War, y'understand."

He tugged reflectively at his ear and Patrice stopped in the middle of unwrapping her snack. She flourished the packet hopefully.

"Was it blue? Really nice with custom leather upholstery?"

The man faintly resembled a turtle when he curved his small mouth down at the corners and settled his head back on his neck. He counted out her change with the plodding slowness of the same species.

"Yeah, yeah. Had a little fellow with him, too. They bought some bait as I recollect. I think I heard 'em say they was goin' up near one of the northwest docks. Don't know if that helps you none."

She flashed a particularly relieved smile. "It helps more than you know. Thank you."

Standing with one sneakered foot inside the car, the breeze fluttering the hem of her blouse worn loose outside her jeans, she waved at him. He waved back. He probably thought she was crazy as he watched her from his window. He might not be too far wrong.

Dusk was tinting the fancifully shaped clouds violet and gray before she found Madison's campsite. It was only a stroke of luck that the couple up the road had noticed the pickup, too, or darkness would have forced her to give up. But the sun, like some artist reluctant to lay aside a painting, was painting the undersides of the cloudy characters a brilliant red. Patrice took advantage of the gorgeous sunset and continued searching.

Miles, weary of fishing, was ambling along the thread of a road gathering rocks when she drove past. She hardly recognized him before he was in her rearview mirror. Slamming on the brakes, she shifted the car into reverse and backed up.

She leaned her head out the window. "Are you hitchhiking?" she teased.

Miles's eyes widened with childlike astonishment. "Wh-where'd you come from?"

"I dropped out of the sky, silly. Get in." She leaned over and opened the opposite door. "Where's your uncle?"

Miles, giggling and covered with dust, climbed in. "Fussin'. The fish haven't bit all day long. He says we can't eat until he catches our supper." The small face crinkled into an adorable frown. "Y'don't think he means it, do you?"

As Patrice followed his elaborate directions for finding the campsite on the lake, she said she didn't think so. Carefully she inched the Ferrari beneath the lazy canopy of trees. She added, as she parked in a protected, out-of-the-way space behind the pickup, that she wasn't about to depend upon his uncle's angling abilities for her dinner!

Madison's talents at fishing seemed to have improved during Miles's absence, however. As the Ferrari snarled to a stop only fifty yards from the water's edge he sat cross-legged before a small fire—a portrait of a virile man quietly at ease with his surroundings.

At the sound of the car, his head lifted. For a moment he regarded them both with intrigued surprise. Grinning, then running his fingers through his tousled hair, he unfolded himself. He hitched at the loose waist of his jeans and gave his knit shirt a casual brushing into place.

"He caught something!" Miles bounded out of the

car in a flash to inspect the cooking fish. "How'd you catch 'em, Madison?" he shouted.

"Pretty easily after I got rid of my little talking machine." Madison chuckled with a curious knitting of his brows at Patrice.

Patrice, not eager to face one of the most difficult tasks of her life, remained where she was in the car. Was it possible that she was about to give Madison a new lease on life by telling him about Rose and shatter the prospects of her own happiness?

Leaning her chin on the window's edge, she blinked up at Madison as he bent low. He braced one hand on the top of the car and scratched at his shadowy beard like a cowpoke.

"Why, ma'am," he drawled, "if I'd known I was going to be blessed with such lovely company, I'd have . . . done something."

"What would you have done?"

He ignored her meaningless question. "What are you going to do first? Get out of the car or tell me what's wrong?"

Putting on her lawyer's air, Patrice smiled. "Now what could possibly be wrong?"

The tip of his index finger brushed the proud tilt of her nose.

"Lady," he said with a solemn intensity, "someday I'm going to knock a dent in that armor of yours. Then what'll you do?"

If he only knew that she had no armor at all where he was concerned! she thought, almost blurting the truth. Instead she grasped his long browned fingers and placed a kiss upon them.

"Can't you be satisfied that I can't live a day without coming after you? I'm chasing after you like a prideless woman, Madison."

Not believing a word of it, he helped her out of the car and shut the door. For a split second he lifted his hand to her face and plunged his gaze headlong into her eyes. Then he brushed a feather-light kiss upon her lips.

"I see you didn't rack up the Ferrari, at least. Congratulations."

Patrice's green eyes danced. "There are times when I think you should have been on that Kawasaki when I backed over it."

He laughed. "Are you hungry?"

Looping her arm through his, she began walking toward the campfire. "Starved."

"I like hungry women," he mumbled wickedly, and fell into step.

The darkness was clawing its way through the trees now, closing them in with velvet shadows. Though Madison smiled and joked with lighthearted amiability, Patrice knew his mind was whirling, juggling facts to figure why she had made the drive.

In the distance, Miles squatted importantly over the fire and arranged the fish frying in the skillet. Their aroma pervaded everything and Patrice's mouth watered. She had forgotten how hungry she was.

Stopping, Madison's features drew into a dark frown. His brows blunted in a doubtful question mark. "Has Justin been hassling you?"

"Of course not," she quickly reassured him. "I told you, that is over. Forever." She changed the subject without warning and clasped her hands to her stomach. "My, I had no idea that fish could be so tempting."

He growled an inaudible remark she guessed she wasn't meant to understand. She didn't think he believed anything she had said.

Miles, mimicking some scene from a bad western movie stood up and banged his fork on the back of a mess kit. "Come and get it!" he yelled boisterously.

Laughing, Patrice shielded her ears.

Madison shrugged. "He doesn't get that from me," he said.

She bent over to peer at the pan filled with crispy

pieces of perch and grew aware of Madison's hand curving casually about the outside of her thigh. Unobtrusively she clasped it to keep it from going further.

"Baked potatoes, too," she exclaimed. "Why, Madison, you're full of surprises."

"I told you a long time ago you needed a good man to take care of you," he retorted.

The bread was hot and buttery and the tartar sauce was just the right tartness to suit Patrice's taste. It was a feast fit for a king. For the next hour she pretended great interest in Miles's culinary niceties and let the brooding man eat his dinner in silence and wonder what had brought her out into the wilds so unexpectedly.

What Patrice didn't know about camp life would have filled several large volumes. Miles spent most of the evening laughing at her inexpertise and went to great lengths to explain how he and Madison had pitched the tent. He proudly demonstrated how to pump the gas lantern to make it glow, and how to scrub up their meager utensils after a simple, though amazingly adequate, dinner.

As the evening turned into night the sound of the night creatures grew louder. The lake had its own peculiar personality, Patrice discovered. Yet the frogs and insects and the occasional splash of a fish soon lost their charm for Miles. Madison seemed quite content to lean against a tree and peel an apple as Miles grew heavy-eyed and silent. Presently however, he rose to lift the weary boy by his shoulders and steer him, mumbling and half asleep, to bed.

Patrice hugged herself and inched nearer the fire. She had no idea where she would sleep, unless it was in her car, but Miles was obviously prepared to spend a good night. She studied Madison's shadow behind the canvas as he settled him down on the army cot. Miles should've been his real son, she thought. After tonight, when she told him what Rose had said, that might be more fact than fancy.

She was stirring in the ashes with a twig when Madison emerged from the tent. Positioning himself beside her shoulder, his leg inches from her cheek, he stood unmoving and gazed down at the top of her head.

The old familiar desire to be loved tingled through her legs. But it was of such a secondary importance now that Patrice dismissed it. It was as if she must begin anew with Madison. Somehow, before she told him the truth, she wished she could rekindle his urgent desire to make her his wife, to build a family about her.

When he lifted one lock of her hair and let it flutter in the firelight, shimmering downward strand by shimmering strand, she didn't think she breathed at all.

"He was tired," she said unnecessarily when the silence grew awkward.

"Yes."

The flames were roasting her cheeks, but not all of the rosy stain was from the fire. She took one long breath, then let it out slowly.

"This is nice. There're a lot of things I don't know."

"There are a lot of things I would like to teach you," he replied softly.

Madison stooped beside her, gripping one of his knees as if it pained him. Settling down beside her, his shoulder casually touching hers, he, too, poked at the crimson coals. The silence limped clumsily, and she made a dozen inane remarks about everything except why she had come.

Far across the lake, miles perhaps, two fishermen called to each other.

Unconsciously Madison rubbed his knees.

Patrice hesitantly placed her own hand on the leg nearest her. When he braced himself back on his palms, she massaged the muscles cording the joints where the surgeon had worked.

"Do they hurt terribly?" she asked as timidly as if she had never touched him before.

"It's the night air. Sometimes it's worse than others."

She gulped a deep breath. "I have to talk to you, Madison."

"I guessed as much."

She was smoothing her fingertips up and down his leg as if she had lost track of what she was doing. "Rose came to see me last night."

He didn't interrupt her as she told her story. He didn't say she had done the right thing. She waited for him to say that having responsibility for Miles would not suffice for not having a wife, that he wanted his own children.

He said nothing.

When she finished he sat up straight. His hands came down on his thighs with the finality of a book slamming closed.

"Say, would you like to walk?"

Stunned, disappointed that he didn't intend to share his feelings, Patrice felt the end of her dreams crowding close. They were suffocating her. Had she really blown it now? Had she told him no so many times that he no longer wanted her for a wife?

She hardly recognized her own voice when she agreed.

Pausing to fetch a worn army blanket from the pickup, Madison wrapped it about her shoulders until she looked like an Indian squaw. "You never make it easy, do you?" he murmured.

She groped in her mind, her head shaking as she wondered what he meant.

"I've been needing to do this since the minute you got here," he said as his mouth came down hard on hers.

Her head snapped back from the ravenous onslaught of his kiss. It was different from anything before—not gentle, not angry, not inquiring, not possessive—only urgent. With his mouth locked to hers he drew one of her arms about his neck and lifted her free of the ground, the blanket trapped between them. Wildly, blindly, she returned his driving hunger with that of her own.

When he finally released her she couldn't keep her balance. Weaving drunkenly, trying to breathe, she clutched the blanket tightly and leaned against the wall of his body.

"What was that for?" she whispered.

He didn't answer immediately but held her up until her legs were functioning properly again. Then he began walking. Some distance from the campsite he turned back. Together they stared across the crook of the lake at the peaceful orange triangle of the tent where Miles slept. He didn't look at her when he spoke.

"I once promised myself that I would hold out for everything with you, Patrice," he said, lowering his gaze to his feet. "I had some crazy idea that marriage would work between us and that I could build a family about you." He shook his head, disillusioned. "I think I must have some of the pioneer left in me—the spirit of the patriarch."

"Madison, you don't understand."

"I'm sure I don't." Snatching his head up, he towered over her in a frowning mixture of desire and loneliness and frustration. "But I'll take it anyway you say. I'll move in. I'll let you move in. Neither of us will move in. I won't ever mention the word marriage or baby again. No commitments, no ties that bind. No nothing. I can't live without you." He crushed her to him so that his mouth was pressed into her hair covering her ear. "I must have you."

How could he not see the issues? How could he not realize what she had told him? Whirling, she threw out her hands, then cried out her agitation.

"Don't you see? Rose has given it to you—what you wanted! In all likelihood Miles is the son you never had! You've won, Madison."

He shaped his hand about his own mouth as he stood

etched against the rawness of the night. He could have been oblivious to everything she had said. She wondered if he were thinking of the war, or of their past love.

He sighed through his fingers then lowered them. "What is a son?" he asked heavily. "What is anything if I don't have you?"

Patrice hovered high above the confusion of her own life, the past days. She looked down on them as being more tangled than the brambles that cluttered the trees looming above them. She felt excessively weary.

Swirling the blanket from her shoulders like a gypsy's cape, she spread it on the ground and dropped down on it in exhaustion. For a moment her forehead rested upon her knees and her hair draped over them.

"Oh, dear God," she breathed. Her eyes closed. "Do you remember the O. Henry story about the man who sold his watch for some combs for his wife's hair when she had sold her hair for a chain for his watch?"

Smiling, Madison lowered himself beside her and drew her hair back behind her ear. Placing a breathy kiss upon its shell, he whispered, "Have we crossed each other's paths somewhere along the way, love?"

She stretched full-length on the blanket and propped her head on her fist. Her fingers absently smoothed the wrinkles from the space of blanket between them.

"All my life I've taken such pride in the fact that I was not a fool."

He, too, braced himself on an elbow. "That, I fear, is in the best of us." He began toying with the buttons on her blouse.

She caught at his hands. "Don't do that."

"Why not?"

She frowned. "Because . . . because we're out here in the middle of the woods, that's why not."

His grin was lustful, even in the darkness. "That's why we should."

"Madison," she protested as he rolled on top of her with a groan.

"Are we going to go through the seduction process again, sweetheart? Because if we are, I've got to take a few shortcuts with you."

With trembling hands Patrice grabbed his head. "Listen to me, Madison." She shook him. "You have serious responsibilities, now, more than ever before."

"Yes."

"Oh, damn it," she breathed. "That's not what I meant to say."

Shoving her hands away, he ignored her fretting and began kissing her neck. The ragged currents of his caress made talking almost impossible.

"I didn't come all the way up here for this," she choked. "I came . . ."

"Will you move in with me?"

"I've made some important decisions, Madison."

"You don't have so many things in that tiny little apartment. I can have you settled in one day." His fingers persisted at undoing the buttons.

"I thought if you still wanted a mother for Miles you might want to think about getting married."

The zipper of her jeans sounded like a buzz saw in the quietness. "If your parents raise a fuss I'll talk to them myself."

"I threw the pills away."

His head came up as if she had slapped him. "What did you say?"

"I said I threw the birth-control pills away. I'll take my—"

"No." He braced his weight on his palms, still sprawled half over her. "The part about Miles and marriage and—"

"A mother for Miles."

"Miles has a mother."

"But—"

"Don't say that word! When?"

"The baby?"

"No! Yes. All right! What d'you mean, baby?"

He was smothering her with kisses, holding her, maneuvering her until she wound up on top of him with her face buried into his chest.

"Now," she said, clinging to him in a sudden wild need to pour out the roiling contents of her heart. "Now!"

She bruised his lips with a heat of passion she didn't dream existed. He tasted so sweet! She could never taste him deeply enough! She ran her tongue over his teeth in wordless, breathless aggression. She met his tongue with hers. Her fingers gripped the sides of his legs as if she could drag him into her own soul. She moved against him, touching him, telling him, pleading with him.

"But darling," he protested when she finally sated her first impulsive thirst, "it'll take a few days. Even in these fast-moving times."

"Forget the marriage. I mean, don't forget the marriage. No, I want it." Her fingers threaded through his hair and she peered down at his mystified love for her. "I want—oh, I want to trust this much. I want a baby. Your baby. I want it now."

"Patrice—"

She was, oddly, near tears. "I don't want to see you hurt anymore, sweet, sweet man. Let me give you this one thing because I love you." She kissed him. And again. "I love you."

She repeated the three words over and over as Madison forcibly pinned her to her back and brushed back her hair from her face with a strange control. Never, not for a second, did he doubt that she loved him. He had known that from the moment he had looked into her eyes that day at the bombing at Bridgeport.

"I thought you'd changed your mind," she choked. "And it was all my fault, and I didn't know how to tell you I have changed."

Suddenly, she stilled. Her eyes fluttered as she contemplated their past. In a slow, perfectly calm voice she said, "You do still want a baby, don't you?"

"Not just any baby, sweetheart. Not Rose's baby. Our baby."

"You want to get married first?"

"Not necessarily. We could fly somewhere and get married tomorrow. But babies don't come just because you snap your fingers."

She was floating on a marvelous, blissful cloud. She laughed softly. "I don't think that's the way you make them, my darling."

He growled a delicious wrath. "You're so smart. I suppose you've arranged your calendar for this."

The smile flirting about her lips was driving him crazy. His hands fanned her waist.

"No," she drew out the word. "Just a minute."

As he finished his task with the buttons of her blouse she dreamily counted on her fingers. "Do you remember my mother's party, the day it rained?"

"Idiot," he said and wrenched his shirt over his head. "How could I forget that?" He crushed her with his weight. "Oh, Patrice, I'm hurting for you," he moaned.

With a fingertip Patrice traced the curve of his fascinating mouth, his chin, his Adam's apple, the splendid bones of his shoulder.

"The day it rained was my last safe day. I'd say my calendar's in pretty good shape."

The time it took Madison to fling her clothes into the velvet grass beyond them was more time than it took for Patrice to consider what she was about to do. She thought, as he filled his arms with her, as he swiftly went that inexorable distance to set a seal upon the past, to begin their future, that she was very blessed.

Life didn't make many promises. This was one covenant she intended to keep with all her strength.

"Well, it isn't raining now," he said hoarsely as he made certain he wasn't moving too quickly for her. "Close your eyes, my little one, and don't think of anything but how I'm loving you. There's nothing for us but the sun."

MORE ROMANCE FOR
A SPECIAL WAY TO RELAX

$1.95 each

MORE ROMANCE FOR
A SPECIAL WAY TO RELAX

LOOK FOR *AN ACT OF LOVE*
BY BROOKE HASTINGS AVAILABLE IN MARCH AND
ENCHANTED SURRENDER BY PATTI BECKMAN
IN APRIL.

Silhouette Special Edition

Coming Next Month

Season Of Seduction by Abra Taylor

In keeping her tennis pro sister out of trouble, Michele Haworth ran into a problem of her own: Damon Pierce—and Damon played to win no matter what the game!

Unspoken Past by Linda Wisdom

Unspoken, but not unremembered. How could Anne ever forget the brief hours she had shared with Kyle Harrison—or his anger when he discovered that she wasn't free to love?

Summer Rhapsody by Nancy John

Nina was leery of British tycoon Dexter Rolfe. But gradually she learned that the fire she found in his arms would warm the years ahead and secure their future together.

Tomorrow's Memory by Margaret Ripy

Cole's vengeful tie to Lacey's past held them together. But the passion they found soon melted their anger and had the Kentucky couple racing toward the future.

Prelude To Passion by Fran Bergen

Operatic set designer Nydia Lear was intrigued by world famous maestro Kurt Klausen. But she had a job to do and no time for love—until Kurt taught her otherwise.

Fortune's Play by Eve Gladstone

In the heat of the Arabian desert, Nicki's marriage to Steve had shattered. But now in Montana, Chinook winds swept across the plains to bring them together . . . this time forever.

Silhouette Romance

15-Day Free Trial Offer
6 Silhouette Romances

6 Silhouette Romances, free for 15 days! We'll send you 6 new Silhouette Romances to keep for 15 days, absolutely free! If you decide not to keep them, send them back to us. You pay nothing.

Free Home Delivery. But if you enjoy them as much as we think you will, keep them by paying the invoice enclosed with your free trial shipment. We'll pay all shipping and handling charges. You get the convenience of Home Delivery and we pay the postage and handling charge each month.

Don't miss a copy. The Silhouette Book Club is the way to make sure you'll be able to receive every new romance we publish before they're sold out. There is no minimum number of books to buy and you can cancel at any time.

READERS' COMMENTS ON SILHOUETTE SPECIAL EDITIONS:

"I just finished reading the first six Silhouette Special Edition Books and I had to take the opportunity to write you and tell you how much I enjoyed them. I enjoyed all the authors in this series. Best wishes on your Silhouette Special Editions line and many thanks."

—B.H.*, Jackson, OH

"The Special Editions are really special and I enjoyed them very much! I am looking forward to next month's books."

—R.M.W.*, Melbourne, FL

"I've just finished reading four of your first six Special Editions and I enjoyed them very much. I like the more sensual detail and longer stories. I will look forward each month to your new Special Editions."

—L.S.*, Visalia, CA

"Silhouette Special Editions are — 1.) Superb! 2.) Great! 3.) Delicious! 4.) Fantastic! . . . Did I leave anything out? These are books that an adult woman can read . . . I love them!"

—H.C.*, Monterey Park, CA